"A first grader exclaimed, 'Tell your friend that she is a good story writer!' We had just finished reading the Jesse Tree stories daily during the Advent season. This collection of Bible history is written with both the teacher and the student in mind. The teacher will find her book useable for any age group. Extension activities are provided, too. The student will find her stories real and inspiring because Anne Neuberger certainly is a good story writer!"

Angela Whitehill
Grade One Teacher
Saint Jude of the Lake
Mahtomedi, MN

"Reminiscent of Madeline L'Engle, Anne Neuberger contemporizes Scripture—specifically the Jesse Tree stories—without sacrificing their poetry. Through practical suggestions for creating a Jesse Tree and beautiful tellings of the Advent stories that populate it, she offers parents, or any adult leader, a way 'to help children develop a stronger sense of who Jesus Christ is and who the people pointing the way to him are.' Children (and adults) can easily forget or neglect the 'waiting, longing, and expectation' that Advent intends. Neuberger's book helps us to remember and to live it."

Jerry Ruff
Editor, *Times Review*,
Diocese of La Crosse newspaper

"Anne E. Neuberger offers parents, teachers, and religious educators practical, down-to-earth, doable ways to build faith and bond families and classes around the Jesse Tree.

"The focus of *Meeting Jesus through the Jesse Tree* is right on target: Building faith within the family should be easy, fun, and a natural part of family life.

"Neuberger's ideas draw out the gift of faith God has given our children, enriching them with stories, heroes, and heroines. Projects require only simple, inexpensive, and easy-to-find materials. Suggestions from the simple to the more challenging allow families and teachers to match creative talent to activities; some are easy, some more challenging, but all are doable.

"The storytelling technique that is employed harkens one back to not just an earlier time in our Judeo-Christian tradition but just a few generations ago in this country, when parents and grandparents—not the TV—were children's storytellers. The optional dialogue script makes the text interactive for children who are already readers. *Meeting Jesus through the Jesse Tree* has potential to bond families, to create memories that will become valued Advent traditions."

Bob Zyskowski
Editor, *The Catholic Spirit*,
Archdiocese of St. Paul-Minneapolis newspaper

"*Advent Stories and Activities: Meeting Jesus through the Jesse Tree* is a wonderful book for parents, catechists, teachers, and all who love and work with children. The first part of the book will be especially valued because of its introduction to the Jesse Tree, coupled with practical ideas of how to create and celebrate a Jesse Tree in a variety of settings. The introduction and suggestions are clear and inviting—exactly what a busy catechist, teacher, or parent needs to get started.

"In Part Two, Stories to Share, Anne does two things particularly well: she provides us with a brief background to the origin of the story in Scripture and hints about how to get the most of the story which follows; and she offers a variety of storytelling styles. The stories are entertaining, thought-provoking and very well-written. I am sure that they will capture the imagination of both the storytellers and the listeners, and draw all into a deeper understanding of and appreciation for the story of Jesus' heritage and birth."

Jackie Witter
Director of Catechesis and Faith Formation
Archdiocese of St. Paul and Minneapolis

"What a fine book! Advent will be greatly enriched by sharing these stories and activities. Anne Neuberger's thoughtful and readable telling of the biblical stories will be appreciated by church and school classes and by families at home. There is a wide range of interest and activities. The dramatic presentation format of some stories encourages participation. This book is a great resource for families who wish to focus on the meaning of Advent."

Carol Erdahl
Co-Owner, The Red Balloon Bookshop

Advent
Stories
and
Activities

Meeting Jesus
through
the Jesse Tree

Anne E. Neuberger

TWENTY-THIRD PUBLICATIONS
Mystic, CT 06355

Acknowledgments

The author would like to thank those who helped make this book possible, including Melissa Johnson, Gwen Costello, Jeanne McPhee, Angie Whitehill, Ann Miller, and her family. Special thanks to her daughter Lucia, whose creativity helped shape the tree variations, and whose enthusiasm for the ancient stories helped bring them to these pages.

Twenty-Third Publications
185 Willow Street
P.O. Box 180
Mystic, CT 06355
(860) 536-2611
800-321-0411

ISBN 0-89622-734-0
Library of Congress Catalog Card Number 96-61817
Printed in the U.S.A.

Dedication

To Leo, Janet, Tobias, and Joyana Jocoby,
family ritualists extraordinaire!

TABLE OF CONTENTS

PART ONE: THE JESSE TREE

PART TWO: STORIES TO SHARE

THE JESSE TREE

An Introduction to the Jesse Tree

Advent. The long night watch, the waiting time, the yearning for the coming of Christmas, and, more fundamentally, for the second coming of Christ.

Each year religion teachers and parents are faced with the challenge of helping children experience this waiting time despite a pervasive atmosphere of instant gratification, a time the secular world calls "the holiday season." Adults often long for the spiritual in a world that moves too fast for reflection, a world that fills whatever time is left with empty values, as portrayed in movies, television, and video games. Parents and teachers can be painfully aware that children are lacking knowledge of their roots and do not know the value of religious rituals and traditions. This is perhaps the most obvious in the weeks before Christmas when the church calls for waiting, longing, and expectation. Where does one start to give Christian children these precious experiences? The ancient communities of Israel handed down their beliefs in the same way that Jesus himself taught: through story.

There is an Advent custom that uses stories to help children develop a stronger sense of who Jesus Christ is and who the people were who pointed the way to him. This custom is called the Jesse Tree. It is a representation of Christ's family tree, suggested by the prophet's words, "There shall come forth a shoot from the root of Jesse" (Isaiah 11:1). This tradition is named for King David's father. Keeping a Jesse Tree includes reading about a biblical person and then fashioning a symbol of that person to place on a tree. As you'll see under "Methods and Materials," there are many ways to depict the "tree."

The creation of a Jesse Tree, however, involves more than telling stories and making symbols. It is a way for children to experience God's presence in their lives. As the stories unfold, as Noah's difficulties, Rachel's concerns, Jonah's frustrations, and Esther's fears become real to listeners, God's plan in their lives becomes clear. The child, on a conscious or subconscious level, can begin to feel this in her or his own life.

Stories provide children with new environments. They give listeners heroes and heroines. Stories introduce abstract ideas such as having a quest and believing in something unseen. Stories can show that seemingly incompetent people can strive and do good, that mistakes can be made and forgiven, that life can be precious and wonderful, even in the midst of adversity. They offer a vocabulary for unexpressed feelings. Stories, then, help children interpret their experiences. They give children a way of experiencing truth that cannot be seen directly.

The Jesse Tree also gives children a sense of salvation history, of the centuries before the birth of Christ, of God's plan and preparation in human history for the birth of Christ. For North American children this is especially important. They are growing up in a young country, a culture whose recorded stories go back just a few hundred years. Yet our religious history goes back much farther. In the United States, we tend to use the word history to mean something that is irrelevant. "Oh, that's history" is a glib way of saying that something doesn't matter anymore, we don't need or want to deal with it. In assuring someone who asks forgiveness of us, we say what happened is history, it's in the past, implying that history is something to move beyond and to forget. But in many other cultures, to label something as history is to say that it is relevant, it is important.

For history *is* important. It tells us what has happened, what we should avoid, why we are who we are and who we are becoming, where we are going and what we may need in the future. Stories from our religious history provide us with a framework for our belief system. These tales, handed down from generation to generation, give us the accumulated wisdom of centuries of living.

To tell children the Jesse Tree stories is to connect them with the countless generations of people who have sought God and experienced God's presence in this world. It is to place our children in the company of people who sought answers to hard questions, who strove to be faithful no matter the difficulties. In telling our children the stories, we give them their place among the people of God.

Note that the twenty-four Scripture-based stories in the second half of this book are *adapted* from the actual Scripture text. The Scripture verses that each story is based on are listed after the title. Some of these stories are told by one of the minor characters in the text, and some are told in the voice of the leading character. If you prefer to read or tell the story directly from the Bible, feel free to do so. You might want to use a children's Bible for younger groups.

Using the Jesse Tree

As we have seen, the essential elements of the Jesse Tree are stories and symbols of those stories. The making of the tree and the creating of symbols can be as simple or as elaborate as time, ages of children, and abilities allow. There are numerous ways to create the tree and symbols, and they can be adapted for various settings and uses.

Wherever and however you make a Jesse Tree, remember the significance of the ancient stories. You are passing on something very precious, making possible a link between the past and the future. Read each story to yourself first, becoming familiar with it so you can then read it aloud, presenting the characters so they come alive through your expression. Tell the stories with reverence, with drama, with humor, and with love.

Families at Home

Jesse Tree stories can be bedtime or dinnertime reading during Advent. Because some of the stories are very long, parents may want to read only parts of each. Or, they may want to read a section at mealtime and the rest at bedtime. After reading the story, spend time with your children to create the symbols. Another method would be for you to pre-make symbols that can be used from year to year (see "Methods and Materials"). After the story is read and the symbol is made, it can ceremoniously be placed on the tree. Either way, a sense of anticipation and of a connection to Jesus is clear.

Some families wait until Christmas Eve to put up their Christmas tree. During Advent, the Jesse tree can stand where the Christmas tree will eventually be, emphasizing that it is a symbol of those who went before Christ, waiting.

Families who put up their Christmas tree early in Advent might want to gradually add the Jesse Tree symbols. Christmas decorations could then be added just before Christmas Eve.

Working with varying ages in a family calls for flexibility. Some older children may be reluctant to participate in the artistic aspects. Reading the stories when the whole family is together, at dinner, or over popcorn some evenings, includes older children and passes on the stories. If they choose not to make symbols, ask them to set up the tree or to assist a younger child. Preschoolers will likely join in with enthusiasm. Their efforts may not yield recognizable symbols, but the groundwork has been laid for an appreciation of the biblical stories. Offer them the same materials as older children, and enjoy their creations, giving them the honor of hanging them on the tree.

Religious Education Classes

Given that classes meet four times in Advent, four to eight stories and symbols could be used. It is helpful to keep the stories you choose in chronological order when presenting them. Decide on a method that best suits the time constraints and abilities of the children. The Scripture verses for stories that cannot be read could be sent home for children and parents to read at home.

For some classes, the Jesse Tree can become the curriculum focus for Advent, leaving ample opportunity for art and story. For situations where time is more limited, a time line or an Advent calendar form will be helpful (again, see "Methods and Materials").

Catholic Schools

In this setting, the Jesse Tree stories can become a central part of daily Advent observances. It will be easier to use all the stories and to create all the symbols, since children gather daily. In classes where the curriculum explores the Old Testament, the Jesse Tree stories will certainly enhance this study.

Methods for making the tree can vary here. The time line or calendar may best suit teachers who want to read the stories but not spend additional class time on symbols. One child could be chosen each day to add to the time line or open the calendar door. However, more involved methods could be used at times—during art classes, for example.

Family Advent Workshops

Jesse Tree stories can be part of a memorable Advent afternoon for families, a community sharing of the ancient tales. The workshop leader can choose which stories to use and participants can choose which symbols to make. If given an assortment of materials, families can be creative in their depictions. Their symbols can be taken home for their own Jesse Trees—thus beginning the tradition at home. Or, you might keep the symbols they make to display on a parish Jesse Tree. Each Sunday in Advent, families could take turns hanging their symbols on the parish tree.

Methods and Materials

The Jesse Tree does not require expensive or elaborate materials. It can be a process that is as simple or as involved as the participants choose. The following are several methods for making the tree and symbols. Select one that works for you, or use the ideas as a springboard for your own plan. Whatever you choose, the most important element is enjoyment: enjoy the stories, enjoy the creativity!

Drawing Your Tree

This is an excellent method for a group with various ages because it is very simple to implement, and everyone can get involved. It can work for families, classrooms, and parish workshops. It tends to be the most calming of the art projects.

First, read the story with the children, then offer them white paper and good pencils, markers, or crayons. One of the charms of this method is that the children bring their own interpretations to the stories, such as war planes flying over David and Goliath or spectacles on Abraham. With very young children, ask them to interpret their drawings for you, and write their words on the back of the drawings. These drawings can be saved and will be a treasure in years to come.

You can display the drawings in a number of ways. Hang them on a tree branch or a Christmas tree, for example, by taping ribbon or thread to two top corners of the paper. Or tape them to a paper tree hung on a wall. You might also hang them by magnets on a tree also held by magnets on a metal surface.

Materials Needed: (For the drawings) Paper, pencils, markers or crayons, thread or ribbon, and tape or magnets. (For the tree) A tree branch secured in a bucket of wet sand, a Christmas tree, or posterboard of green or brown.

Making an Advent Calendar

Many children are familiar with Advent calendars, opening a little door each day in Advent as they count down to Christmas. This idea can easily be adapted for a Jesse Tree. Since the calendar has to be made before Advent, it works well for families who don't have time for a daily art project or for religion classes where time is restricted.

On a white or light colored piece of posterboard (standard size is 28" x 22"), draw a tree. An evergreen is easiest to draw and offers more symbol space than a deciduous tree. Keep the tree very simple. Outline it with a green marker.

The "doors" can be made with small sheets of paper and tape, but small notepads with a strip of adhesive (Post-It Notes) are the most convenient. (The 3" square pads work best with this size poster.) Place 24 of these squares on the tree. Number the doors, 1-24, placing number 1 on the base of the tree, and number 24 on the top (where a star is placed on a Christmas tree). Under each door, directly on the poster, draw a symbol for each story with bright markers. Use the Table of Contents to see the order of the stories. The names of the main characters can also be written there.

Hang the poster and, after reading a story, have children guess the symbol and open the door. The doors can be taken off entirely, so that, little by little, the tree is decorated with colorful symbols. A child as young as eight can create this, and the poster can be saved from year to year.

There are others ways to use the calendar: the symbols (and corresponding numbers) can be placed randomly on the tree, as they are on an Advent calendar, or the doors can be unnumbered and a door could be chosen each day and the story read after the symbol is found.

Materials Needed: One sheet of white or light colored posterboard, a pencil, markers of various bright colors (including green), twenty-four three-inch square sheets of paper and tape (or Post-It Notes), and tacks for hanging the poster.

Using a Time Line
Some children take great delight in symbols, while others will be more interested in the historical aspects of the Jesse Tree. A time line works best for those interested in the history, and it is also a good method for situations where time is limited.

Using a roll of paper, such as shelf paper, create a time line by attaching a length of the paper to a long wall. You will need approximately six feet, allowing for about three inches per story. Draw a horizontal line with a bold marker, with a two-inch vertical line protruding from this line every three inches. There should be twenty-three of the vertical lines, with the twenty-fourth, the one that represents Christ, at the end.

Read a story or two a day, and put the corresponding names in order on the line. The main character's name, the name of the story, or the Scripture citation could be used. In a classroom with children who can write legibly, students can take turns adding the names. Symbols can also be used, but keep space restrictions in mind. Using a variety of colors for the names, etc., adds visual interest as the time line progresses. When all the stories have been read and the name or symbol of

Christ is added at the end of the line, add an arrow extending from the existing line and write the names of the children involved. This is a concrete way for them to see that they, too, are part of Christ's lineage.

Materials Needed: A roll of paper, at least eight inches wide, a ruler, markers, and tape or tacks to secure the paper to the wall.

Three-Dimensional Decorations
This method is perhaps the most enticing to those with artistic abilities. After reading stories, provide participants with such materials as multicolored pipe cleaners, self-hardening clay, craft sticks, felt, glitter, and sequins, and encourage freestyle creativity.

This method works well during a parish Advent workshop, or for Advent Sundays at home. Provide lots of time, perhaps some snacks, and plenty of room for creativity. The symbols created will vary as greatly as the number of participants and will make a delightful display. A tree branch from a deciduous tree, secured in a bucket of sand, makes an excellent tree. An undecorated Christmas tree would also work.

Materials Needed: Scissors, tape, rulers, needles, pens, markers, staplers, ribbons, streamers, various colors of tissue and construction paper, pipe cleaners, thread, wire, self-hardening clay, craft sticks, felt and other fabrics, glue (white and colored), glitter, glitter pens, fabric paints, sequins, buttons, etc., and some type of sturdy tree for display.

Creating a Medallion Tree
This method involves decorating a tree branch with clay medallions (hung with colorful ribbons). Because of the time involved in making medallions, you might want to prepare them before Advent begins. To create them, work on waxed paper on a smooth surface. Roll out self-hardening clay as you would cookie dough, to a 1/8-inch thickness. Cut into circles (jar covers, about three inches in diameter, work well). With a rounded toothpick, draw a symbol for each story into the clay, taking care not to push the toothpick all the way through. The name of the story character can also be added near the bottom. At the top center, make a hole in the clay large enough for a thin ribbon to be pushed through. Allow the medallions to dry away from a heat source, turning them daily. They will dry in three to four days. Pull colorful ribbon through the hole on each one. After you share each story, have a child ceremoniously hang the medallion on your tree.

Materials Needed: Self-hardening pottery clay, waxed paper, a rolling pin, table knives, three-inch jar covers or round cookie cutters, rounded toothpicks, trays for drying, thin ribbon of various bright colors, and a tree for display.

Making Felt Banners

A banner with detailed ornaments symbolizing the Jesse Tree stories can be a family or class treasure. To make the banner, cut out a 82" x 36" piece of neutral-colored felt. Fold over two inches along the top edge to form a casing and stitch. With green felt, cut an evergreen tree shape. A tree that is 25" tall and 23" at the widest point will fit onto this size banner. With a brown, black, or tan felt piece, cut a trunk. Glue or stitch the tree and trunk onto the banner. Slip a dowel into the casing.

To make the symbols, use felt pieces and fabric scraps of varying colors to fashion small (no bigger than 3" x 3") symbols for each story. These can be made in the actual shape of the symbol or be glued on to a square, rectangle, circle, or half-circle base. Several colors of felt can be used on each symbol, and glitter can also be added, however this may make the symbol too heavy to adhere to the banner. A small snap, or bit of Velcro Hook and Loop sewed on the back can remedy this.

Materials Needed: (For the banner) Felt fabric in a neutral color (measuring 28" x 36"), green felt for the tree (measuring at least 25" in length and 23" in width), a few inches of brown, black, or tan felt for the trunk, fabric scissors, pencils, ruler, glue, a needle and thread or a sewing machine, a half-inch thick dowel thirty inches long. (For the symbols) Felt squares and pieces of felt in various colors (red, blue, purple, yellow, gold, black, green lighter than the tree felt, pink, tan, brown, etc.), sequins, "eyes," glitter, markers, snaps or Velcro Hook and Loop if necessary.

A Jesse Tree Booklet

If your children or class enjoys writing, first read the Bible story and then challenge children to rewrite it in their own words. Invite them to illustrate the story in any way they wish. At the end of Advent bind these pages together to form a Jesse Tree booklet.

This method can be used with any of the other methods or by itself. A drawback is that it does not create a visual focus (as a tree would), and symbolism may or may not be part of the child's creation. However, it does encourage children to listen intently and to interpret the stories in a more personal way.

Materials Needed: Notebooks and pencils or pens (or use individual sheets of paper that you can bind with yarn at the end of Advent).

SYMBOL SUGGESTIONS

The stories may suggest different symbols to different listeners. Here are just a few possibilities that could be adapted to the activities described in "Methods and Materials":

Creation: moon over water, earth

Adam and Eve: fruit, tree, snake

Noah: ark, rainbow

Abraham: stars

Sarah: tent, bread

Jacob: ladder, angels

Rachel and Leah: three hearts, entwined

Joseph: twelve brothers, coat

Moses: baby in a basket, tablets of Ten Commandments, burning bush

Ruth: wheat or barley sheaves

Samuel: temple

David: harp

Solomon: crown

Elijah: raven, chariot

Isaiah: tongs of fire and coal

Nehemiah: wall

Jonah: fish, ship

Esther: jewels

Tobias: angel, fish

Daniel: lion

Zechariah and Elizabeth: incense burner, angel

Mary: a figure on a donkey, a rose, a ship

Joseph: hammer, saw

Jesus: star, stable, manger

PART TWO

STORIES TO SHARE

Creation | Adam & Eve | Noah | Abraham | Sarah, Abraham & Isaac | Jacob | Solomon | Elijah

The Story of Creation

(Based on Genesis 1, 2:1–4)

Introduction

The first story for the Jesse Tree is from a time before time. It is a story about how the world and its order came to be. Many cultures have stories such as this, but the Israelites' story of creation centered not just on the actual creation of the universe, but on God's love and care. Creation is the first saving act of God, it is God's pledge to the future. To the Israelites, saved from slavery in Egypt, the creation story illustrated why God intervened for them. They could look at the mercy God had shown them and know that this was not the first time—and they believed that it would not be the last time. Through the creation story, God's love and mercy could be traced back, before Abraham and Sarah, even before Noah.

This is a wonderful story for a dramatic reading. Do not hesitate to speak softly, then more loudly for effect. Involve your listeners, too, by encouraging them to chant the lines, "That was the first day," etc. A simple signal, such as holding up the appropriate number of fingers to indicate which day, lets children know when to join in.

The Story Begins

Long, long ago, in a time before time, there was God, the Creator. There were no sounds, no colors, no laughter. There was only darkness over the deep, and God's spirit hovered over the water.

God said, "Let there be light."

Brilliant light burst forth, piercing the darkness! God saw that the light was good, and separated the light from the darkness. God called the light "day" and the dark "night."

All: That was the first day.

God said, "Let there be a great space above the waters." A space formed wide and blue, stretching over the waters. God called the space "sky."

All: That was the second day.

God said, "Let dry land appear." The waters moved over, gushed away, and rushed forward until land came forth, forming mountains, prairies, deserts, and forests. Trees, grasses, and flowers graced these places. God called the land "earth" and the waters "seas." And God saw that it was good.

All: That was the third day.

God said, "Let there be lights in the sky." In the blueness of the sky, a fiery ball appeared, which was the sun. At night, the pearly, paler moon appeared, and stars danced across the darkness.

All: That was the fourth day.

God said, "Let the waters be filled with fish." Then, large sleek fish, small quick ones, multicolored ones, and softly hued ones swam the seas.

God said, "Let the air be filled with birds." The sky was filled with the songs and flight of millions of birds, and the trees were adorned with their nests.

All: That was the fifth day.

God said, "Let there be other animals." Lumbering, mooing cows appeared, along with scampering squirrels, slithering snakes, quick lizards, graceful deer, prowling cats, howling wolves.

God then said, "Let there be humankind." And God created humans, male and female. They emerged from the love of God, radiant and beautiful, for they were made in God's image. God saw all that was now created, and indeed, it was very good.

All: That was the sixth day.

On the seventh day, God rested.

The Story of Adam & Eve

(Based on Genesis 3)

Introduction

*How did life come to be as it is? There is so much beau-
ty in life, yet there is much pain, so often there is
laughter and there are also overwhelming difficulties. Why? This is a question people ask in each
generation, for it is part of being human. One way
to look for direction is through stories.*

*Genesis 2 and 3 tell the stories of Adam and Eve
and the Fall. Like the creation story, these stories are
a reflection of the Israelite people's experience of God.
The authors were trying to portray how sin began, and
how it flows into history, changing the human condition
from a pure to a fallen state. These stories sketched characters that every reader could identity with.*

*The name "Adam" comes from a pun on the Hebrew word "adamah," meaning soil and
man. It can refer to one man, but often is used as a collective term for humankind. Eve
appropriately means "life" or "to live."*

*All cultures have lore involving a rule, something forbidden. The protagonist disobeys
this rule and thereby changes the right order of things. In this story, the fruit was eaten,
there was an abuse of freedom, and so Adam and Eve were turned out of the Garden of
Eden and the unhappiness and sin of the world began. Adam and Eve had become their
own god, thus causing what seemed to be a permanent separation from God, the source of
all life. Without God, death, sorrow, and sin resulted. The story of the Fall teaches that sin
abounds. It sets the stage for salvation and for Christ's coming. It illustrates that even
though sin abounds, so does God's love.*

*A good way to engage children in this story is through symbols. Before reading the story
aloud, hold up simple drawings of these symbols: a tree, a fruit, a snake, an angel. Ask the
children to listen for what the symbols mean in the story. When you have finished reading, discuss these meanings and ask listeners which ones best symbolize the story for
them. Another way to engage children is to have them enter the story when there is dialogue. Should you want to do this, the "parts" are marked appropriately.*

The Story Begins

Eve and Adam, the first woman and man, lived happily in the garden that God had made for them. All around them were trees with sweet fruits to eat. Gentle animals roamed the land. It was neither too hot nor too cold. The first woman and man did not work for their food, nor did they get sick or hurt. God gave them everything they needed, and they lived happily in the garden.

God made only one rule: they were not to eat the fruit from one certain tree, a tree in the middle of the garden. They were not to touch it, or they would die. Everything else they could eat. That was the only rule.

One day, Eve was out walking and she met the snake. Now the snake was a clever animal, and knew how to play tricks.

Snake: "Did God really say you can't eat from the fruits of that tree?"

Eve: "Oh, no, we can eat from any of the trees. I especially love that fruit, over there."

She pointed to a fig tree nearby. The snake waited. Eve went on, as the snake knew she would.

Eve: "There is only one fruit we cannot eat, from the tree in the middle of the garden."

Snake: "Why not?"

Eve: "We are not even to touch it. For if we do, we will die."

The snake chuckled.

Snake: "No, you'll not die! You were told that because God knows that on the day you eat it, you will be like gods—you will know good and evil."

Good and evil? Be like God? Eve pondered this as she walked over to the forbidden tree. She was curious. She wanted to understand more things, and if the snake was right, maybe this fruit would help her.

The snake watched silently as Eve stood under the tree. She peered at the fruit. It looked as good as any other fruit she had eaten, perhaps better. It was beautiful to look at. Eve appreciated beauty, even though it surrounded her. She looked around. No one was looking, at least as far as she could tell.

She reached up, then stopped as she heard Adam's footsteps. She looked at Adam, then again reached up, plucking the fruit from the tree. She took two, one for herself and one for Adam.

They each took a bite.

And nothing was ever the same again.

Eve gasped. Adam started.

They realized that they were naked, so quickly they took the leaves from a fig tree and fashioned clothing to cover their bodies.

Suddenly they heard the sound of God walking in the garden.

Eve and Adam then did something they had never done before: they hid. They hid, feeling something they had never felt before: shame.

God: "Where are you? I have heard your voices. Adam?"

Adam called out from his hiding place.

Adam: "I was afraid because I was naked, so I hid."

God: "Who told you that you were naked? Have you been eating the fruit I told you not to eat?"

Adam: "It was Eve! She gave me the fruit, and I ate it."

God: "Eve, what have you done?"

From her hiding place Eve protested.

Eve: "The snake tempted me, so I ate it."

God: "For this, you will now know pain and unhappiness. You will work hard for your food. Children will not come to you easily, but only through pain. You will have discomforts, you will know sickness, and you will someday die."

Then Adam and Eve lost their feelings of peace and harmony. They were given animal skins for clothing and sent out of the garden. No more could they eat without working. No more would they have only laughter and joy.

Outside of the garden, Eve shivered. It was the first time she had felt cold. Adam, who was always naming things, said:

Adam: "This feeling—let's call it cold."

Then he looked at Eve, and there were tears on her cheeks.

Eve: "And this feeling—let's call it sad."

So, now cold and sad, they stopped and looked back to the garden. There a magnificent cherubim stood guarding the entrance to the garden. They would never get back in again.

Ahead of them, the ground was covered with thistles and brambles. Together they looked around at the barrenness.

What, Eve wondered, would they do now?

The Story of Noah

(Based on Genesis 6:5–22, 7, 8, 9:1–17)

Introduction

Noah, a descendant of Eve and Adam, may have been a tent dweller and a skilled craftsman. He was a man of integrity who closely followed the ways of God, a just man in an unjust world. By Noah's time, wickedness had taken over the earth that had been at its creation so good. God chose to destroy everything in order to preserve what was right, and start over. Only Noah and his family and some animals were chosen to survive the great flood. Noah's son Shem is listed in the genealogy of Jesus in the Gospel of Luke.

Following are two versions of this beloved story, one rich with details to challenge the imagination, and the other a shorter version for younger, wigglier listeners. Before reading either version, give each child a piece of construction paper and assign one of these animals to each (all are mentioned in the story): monkeys, snakes, spiders, zebras, giraffes, bees, tapirs, crocodiles, tigers, goats, squirrels, lizards, opossums, deer, rabbits, antelope, cows, birds, bears. Invite children to draw their animal and put its name on the picture. Ask them to listen for their animal's name as you read the story, raising their pictures when theirs is mentioned. For those who want to use the longer version of this story, I have divided it into "chapters" so you can read it all at once or read it chapter by chapter.

Chapter One: Deborah Remembers

The rolling hills were very green. The grape vines grew strong and vigorous. Noah walked in his vineyard, inspecting the vines, delighting in them.

Nearby sat his daughter-in-law, Deborah, who had married Shem. She sat in the sunshine, nursing her tiny son, Aram. Noah moved on, and she watched his happiness. She knew how he felt. Each spring she felt thankful for all her blessings, especially that the horrible flood was over. Never again would they need to climb back into the ark and take shelter. Any rains that came now were gentle, life-giving rains. God had promised.

She remembered the day that Noah had told them of the coming flood. His face was solemn and worried. God had spoken to him about how wicked humans had become. Only Noah and his family were faithful to God. Everyone would perish in a great flood except Noah and his family. And the animals.

Chapter Two: Building the Ark

And so, Noah and his wife, their sons Shem, Japheth, and Ham, and their wives built a boat called an ark that was so large, so towering, that it had three decks on it! Noah and his sons toiled many long days sawing lumber, hammering, fitting. The women worked on the inside, smearing pitch from trees over every crack. It was filthy, hot, sticky work. And outside, people watched, laughing and making fun of them.

Deborah had marveled at the size of the ark. It was the largest thing in town. Soon, however, she and her sisters-in-law began dreading the teasings from the onlookers. Noah and their husbands seemed so foolish, working out under a cloudless sky. A flood? Rain didn't even seem likely. She began to wonder herself if Noah had just imagined this message from God. But still, she worked beside her mother-in-law, spreading the pitch.

Next, they began to gather food, enough for many months. Bags of wheat and fruit filled corners of the awkward ark. They ran up and down the plank, lugging food, toting drinking water, carrying blankets and clothing, but the sky remained cloudless.

Noah worked tirelessly. He never questioned if what he did was foolish. He was doing as God had directed. But the hardest work was yet to come.

"We must gather the animals," Noah told them. "We need to get two of every kind, a female and a male. Then, they must go on the ark, along with the kinds of food they need," Noah said.

The three brothers sighed. Was this even possible?

But God was with them and so it was. Little by little, the animals were found, and brought to the ark: *monkeys*, (pause slightly after naming each) *snakes, spiders, bees, tapirs, crocodiles, tigers, goats, squirrels, lizards, rabbits, antelope, cows, birds, bears, zebras, giraffes, opossums, deer*......on and on. Shem searched, Ham looked,

Japheth explored. They brought back animals that resisted them, bit them, kicked them, stung them, flew away from them. Deborah helped gather grasses, nuts, hay, and anything else she thought the animals would eat. How much did they need? God must guide her, she decided.

Finally the animals were all together. Such beauty! Look at the touch of bright red on that *blackbird's* wing and the pattern on the *zebra's* back! The length of the *giraffe's* neck was astounding! No wonder the ark needed to be so large!

What chaos as the family pushed and coaxed the animals into the ark! The squawks and squeals, brays and neighs were deafening. The gangplank sagged under the weight of the elephants. Quickly it became slippery with animal droppings. Soon the inside of the ark would be as dirty. How would they ever live with the smell?

But threatening clouds were rolling in now. The air was cooler, the wind picking up. Noah called his family together and they walked up the plank together. It was God who shut the door.

At the sound, they paused. Some of the animals became frightened to be closed in, and the humans were afraid too. Already they heard the rain on the roof.

Chapter Three: The Rain Poured Down

The rain fell as if in buckets. It rained all day. It rained all night. The sound of the steady drumming on the roof made it difficult to sleep. After several days, Deborah realized that the ark was no longer on the ground. It was floating! She fed the animals, marveling that so much rain could have fallen that they were now afloat. She was glad they had put such great care into sealing the ark! It was hard to walk as the boat moved and the animals seemed more frightened than ever. Deborah made soothing sounds as she fed the *opossums*. She stroked the sleek *deer*, and sang a little to the cowering *rabbits*.

It was dark in the ark, even during the day. But Noah's family was still cheerful, grateful to be saved. As they gathered to eat, they prayed, told stories, and sang songs. Ten days went by. It rained all day, and it rained all night. Twenty days went by, and it still rained. The animals were no longer frightened, but they were weak from no exercise, and Deborah worried about them. The family became quiet. No more songs and stories. Still they prayed, a "help-us-God" kind of prayer.

Thirty-five days passed, and still it rained. Thirty nine days…then one night, the fortieth night, Deborah woke up. She felt Shem was awake, too.

"What is it?" she whispered. "Is there something wrong?"

"I don't hear the rain!" he whispered back.

She sat up. She had become so used to the sound of the rain after forty days and forty nights that she did not recognize silence. "It has ended!" she whispered.

For a moment, she and Shem held hands, savoring the quiet. Then they jumped up and woke the others. There were cries of delight, tears of joy, and prayers of gratitude.

Chapter Four: Water, Water Everywhere

In the morning they all crowded around the window to see outside for the first time in forty days. Water was everywhere. The huge ark now seemed small, for it held all of life that remained on the earth! It was like a seed floating on the water.

"Where are the trees?" asked her sister-in-law.

"We are above the trees," answered the mother.

"We are above the mountains!" Shem said.

They were silent then, knowing it would be a long, long time before they could leave the ark.

Still, Deborah sang again. There was hope. They could smell fresh air! After a few weeks, the top deck of the ark was no longer under water. They scrubbed it and hung wash. The clothing flapping in the breeze was a sign of life to her.

When the second deck was useable, they feasted there. The *cats, rabbits, lizards,* and *squirrels* ran around now. Babies were being born every hour. The noise and stench in the animals' quarters was overwhelming, but it was full of new life, and no one complained.

Many more days passed as they watched the water recede. Soon they would see tree tops! Noah took a *dove* to the deck and let it go. Deborah watched, for the sweet *doves* were her favorites.

The *bird* soared into the air, and Deborah's spirits rose with it. Never again would she take for granted the sight of a free *bird* in the sky! But in an hour it returned. It had found nowhere to land.

Sadly, they went back to their chores. A week later, Noah tried this again. The *dove* was gone for a long time.

"I see it! It's coming back!" she called to the others. "And look! It has something it its mouth!" The *dove* carried a new, fresh olive branch in its beak!

What rejoicing there was that night!

Another week passed, and again Noah sent the *dove* out. Every one went about their work, but they all watched the deck where it might return. It never came back!

Chapter Five: Time to Leave the Ark

Some weeks later God spoke to Noah, saying it was time to leave the ark. Noah lifted the door and they gazed out onto dry land. It was beautiful! The family said a thanksgiving prayer.

The animals swarmed out then, the large and the small, the awkward and the graceful: *monkeys, snakes, spiders, zebras, giraffes, bees, tapirs, crocodiles, tigers, goats, squirrels, lizards, opossums, deer, rabbits, antelope, cows, birds, bears.* All had young with them. Deborah smiled as she watched them go. Smell and all, she had loved them.

She and Shem held hands as they descended from the ark.

Within her, too, new life was stirring. Soon she would give birth, and her child would be born on the land.

Deborah smiled at the baby in her arms, kissing him on the top of his head. A light rain had begun to fall, and Noah came to join her. She covered the baby with her shawl but she enjoyed the mist on her face. Still the sun shone a little, and within minutes, a rainbow appeared in the sky.

"Look!" she said to Noah. "A rainbow, just like the day we left the ark!"

Noah smiled and took the baby from her. He held the child up and showed him the rainbow. "See? See the rainbow? That is God's sign to us that there will never be another great flood. That is God's covenant with us and with you and with your children and your children's children's children."

And the baby laughed and clapped his hands.

SHORTER VERSION

Long, long ago, the people of the earth turned their backs on God. Only Noah and his family were good and loving. God told Noah to build a huge, strong boat called an ark, and to find two of each kind of animal and take them onto the ark. Soon God would send a terrible flood, and only Noah and his family, and the animals on the ark would survive.

Noah's family worked hard to build the ark and even harder to catch the animals. Little by little, they filled the ark with two *monkeys, snakes, spiders, zebras, giraffes, bees, tapirs, crocodiles, tigers, goats, squirrels, lizards, opossums, deer, rabbits, antelope, cows, birds,* and *bears,* and all the other kinds of animals. Oh, the braying, chattering, barking, and howling that filled the ark!

Then the rain began to fall. It rained for forty days and forty nights. Noah fed the *monkeys, snakes, spiders, zebras, giraffes, bees, tapirs, crocodiles, tigers, goats, squirrels, lizards, opossums, deer, rabbits, antelope, cows, birds,* and *bears,* and all the other animals. He cleaned up after them, and he tried to sleep. Each day, he hoped the rain would end soon.

Finally, all was quiet. The rain had stopped! Slowly, slowly, the water went down, and after many days, Noah was able to open the door. Out ran the *monkeys, snakes, spiders, zebras, giraffes, bees, tapirs, crocodiles, tigers, goats, squirrels, lizards, opossums, deer, rabbits, antelope, cows, birds,* and *bears.* Out ran Noah and his family! And in the sky was a beautiful rainbow, a sign of God's promise that there would never again be such a great and terrible flood.

The Story of Abraham

(Based on Genesis 12:1–7, 15:1–6)

Introduction

Abraham was the first of the great leaders whose family of faith is traced to Jesus. His name means "father," and he is known as the first of the patriarchs. All around him, others were worshiping gods of wood and clay, but Abraham was called by Yahweh (the proper name of the God of Israel) to begin a new nation of believers. One of the most important characters in the Old Testament, Abraham teaches that God is calling us, and that our response should be love and trust. Even as we see Abraham leading us toward Christ's story, it is important to keep in mind that Jews and Moslems, as well as Christians, trace their history to Abraham.

Before reading the following tale, practice with the child who will be speaking for "God." Remember to give this story all the drama it deserves. After reading the story, help children to make or trace and decorate a large star. On one side they can print their name, and on the other side these words: "God has a plan for me, too."

The Story Begins

Outside the tent, the flocks of sheep and herds of cattle were making noises with their animal voices. Servants moved through the groups of tents, going about their daily work. Nearby, beautiful, beloved Sarah kneaded bread. Abraham watched his wife, then looked out onto all that he owned. Yes, Abraham was a wealthy man in many ways.

But now it was time for his prayers. As he started to pray, Abraham heard a voice calling him.

God: "Abraham, leave this land, the land of your parents, and go to a land I will show you. I will make of you a great nation, and I will bless you. I will bless those who bless you and curse those who curse you. All the communities of the earth shall find blessing in you."

Now Abraham was a faithful man. He loved God very much. If God asked him to leave this land he knew, move all the people and animals to another, unknown, place, Abraham knew he must go—no matter how hard it was.

So, sheep bleating, cows mooing, babies crying, tents folded, Abraham and Sarah's household began to move. When they reached the land of Canaan, God again spoke to Abraham.

God: "To your descendants, I will give this land."

Abraham built an altar there, to honor God, but he was puzzled. What did God mean by his descendants? Abraham and Sarah had no children. Still, Abraham trusted God. His large group moved from time to time, and they met many other people and worked out various problems. They kept the ways of the Lord, and loved God.

A few years passed this way. One day, Abraham was again in his tent, praying. God appeared to him.

God: "Fear not, Abraham, for I will reward you for all your faithfulness."

Despite this faithfulness, Abraham did ask God, "What good will your gifts be, if I have no children? I keep your ways, I pray, I try to do as you ask. But if Sarah and I have no children, how can we pass on your blessings?"

God: "Go outside, Abraham."

Abraham stepped out into the cool night. It was cloudless, and the sky was strewn with stars.

God: "Look up, Abraham. Count the stars."

Abraham knew he could not count all the stars in that magnificent sky.

God: "All those stars will be the number of your descendants."

The night was quiet, the stars shone overhead. Abraham knew that nothing is impossible with God. He must be content to wait to see what God's plan was for him.

The Story of Sarah

(Based on Genesis 18:1–15, 21:1–7)

Introduction

Sarah, Abraham's cherished and beautiful wife, traveled with him, enduring the hardships and uncertainty of this strange journey. At one point, when they entered Egypt, she was taken from Abraham to become a wife of the pharaoh. God intervened, and together she and Abraham left Egypt. But the greatest trial of Sarah's life was her inability to have children, for she lived in a society that looked down on women who did not have children. She resorted to having her handmaid, Hagar, give birth to Abraham's child, Ishmael. But God rewarded Sarah for her faithfulness, and joy and laughter came her way when she no longer expected it.

In this story, Sarah experiences many emotions: she is calm, bewildered, astounded, skeptical, frightened, and joyful. Discuss these words with the children, and post them so all can read them. Then ask the listeners to raise their hands when they recognize one of these feelings in Sarah's story.

The Story Begins

It was the hottest part of the day. All was quiet with Abraham and Sarah's household, for it was too warm to work or play. Even the animals felt drowsy. Sarah rested inside the tent, and Abraham sat just outside the door.

"Sarah!" Abraham called suddenly. "It looks as if we are getting company!"

Peeking out, Sarah saw Abraham running towards three strangers. Who could they be? Why would they be traveling now, in this heat?

Abraham had reached them, and was bowing to the ground.

"I beg you kindly do not pass us by. I will have water brought to you, and we will share our bread with you before you go on," Sarah heard Abraham say.

The strangers agreed. Who would resist Abraham's hospitality? Sarah smiled *joyfully* as she watched Abraham hastening towards her. Now he would involve her.

She stepped away from the door and Abraham burst in. "Hurry! Make bread! We have company!" he exclaimed excitedly. "I'll go and see to the other arrangements."

He hastened off to have a servant prepare meat, and he gathered cream and milk. Sarah *calmly* mixed and stirred. Her hands covered with flour, she stayed in the tent, but listened as Abraham and the three guests settled into the shade near the tent.

"Where is your wife, Sarah?" one guest asked.

Sarah paused. How did this stranger know her name?

"In the tent," Abraham said. "She is preparing bread for us."

"I will visit you this time next year, and Sarah will have a son," the guest said.

Sarah stopped kneading the bread dough. She was *astounded*. She was to have a baby? For years she had longed for a child, but now she was too old. She was *bewildered*. And so she was also *skeptical*. It wasn't possible! The idea was so absurd, Sarah laughed softly to herself.

"Why did Sarah laugh and say 'am I really to have a child now that I am too old?'" the stranger asked Abraham.

Sarah put her floury hands to her mouth. Had she spoken out loud? No! Who was this stranger who knew miraculous things? Who was he that he knew her thoughts?

"Is anything too wonderful for our God?" the stranger said. "At the same time next year, you and Sarah will have a son."

Now fear flooded Sarah. Was Abraham speaking to an angel? To Yahweh, their God? *Frightened*, she called out, "I did not laugh!"

And the stranger replied, "Oh, yes you did!"

But God was not angry with Sarah for laughing, but looked kindly upon her. Within the year, Sarah, in her old age, gave birth to a baby boy.

They were inspired by God to name him Isaac, which means "May God laugh in delight." Sarah laughed *joyfully* again, saying, "God has given me cause to laugh! All those who hear of this will laugh with me!"

And Abraham and Sarah rejoiced in their son, and taught him the ways of the Lord.

The Story of Jacob

(Based on Genesis 25:19–28, 27:1–29, 28:10–22)

Introduction

When Isaac was of marriageable age, Abraham sent a servant back to the land of his birth to find a wife for his son. Through God's help, the servant brought back Rebekah. Isaac and Rebekah loved one another, but as with Isaac's parents, much time passed before Rebekah became pregnant. She carried twin boys, Esau and Jacob, who fought inside her even before she gave birth. God told Rebekah that these babies would someday become leaders of two countries, and that the second-born twin would be master over his brother.

When the brothers reached adulthood, Jacob and Rebekah tricked Esau out of his birthright, causing Jacob to leave his homeland, fleeing Esau's anger. On this journey, Jacob encountered God who pledged to Jacob what was promised to his grandfather Abraham years before. And, like his grandfather, Jacob accepted Yahweh as his God, worshiping and following the one true God of Abraham and Isaac.

This story lends itself to speaking parts. An adult should be the narrator, telling the bulk of the story. Choose one child to speak God's words, another Jacob's. Practice with the readers beforehand, encouraging them to read with expression.

The Story Begins

Narrator: Jacob walked on and on as the sun slipped from the sky. He knew he would not reach his uncle's house before nightfall, and soon he must find a place to sleep. Thoughts of home, memories of the last three days, weighed on him as he pushed on. He would sleep later.

Jacob had tricked his father and his brother. He had to admit that. But, it had been his mother's idea. She wanted Jacob to have their father's blessing, to receive the power to lead the family when Isaac died. Together they had tricked the nearly blind, elderly Isaac into thinking Jacob was really Esau. Esau was so angry, he had threatened to kill Jacob, and now Jacob was journeying all alone, fleeing from Esau, heading for his Uncle Laban's home.

When he was a child, Jacob had heard his mother tell how he and his twin brother had fought even in her womb. Esau had been born first, but he, Jacob, arriving just minutes later, had been clutching his brother's heel. Jacob had been trying to catch up to Esau ever since. Even though they were twins, they had nothing in common. Esau loved to hunt. He was rarely home, but off with his quiver and bow. He brought home delicious wild game, which their father Isaac enjoyed. Jacob was quieter, he preferred staying at home, working with the domestic animals.

But here he was, on the road, and Esau was comfortably at home. It was dark now. Not bothering with a fire, Jacob ate a cold dinner, and looked about for a good place to sleep. There was a pile of stones nearby. He took one, and lay down, using the rock for a pillow. He pulled his cloak around him to keep off the night chill. After the long day's walk, it was easy to fall asleep.

Soon he was dreaming. Jacob saw a ladder standing on the ground. He looked up but the top of the ladder reached up and up into the heavens. This was no empty ladder. There were angels of God going up and down the steps! Jacob watched these beautiful figures moving gracefully.

Then, he dreamed he saw God standing over him, saying,

God: "I am the Lord, the God of Abraham and the God of Isaac. I will give to you and to your children and grandchildren the land that you lie on now. Your descendants will be so many, they will be like the specks of dust on the ground. These people will spread to the west and the east, to the north and to the south. Know that I am with you. I will keep you safe wherever you go, and bring you back to this land, for I will not desert you."

Narrator: Jacob sat up. The dream was gone, but the feeling was not. He exclaimed,

Jacob: "What a holy place this is!"

Narrator: He looked around, feeling a little afraid. Then he said,

Jacob: "Surely God is here and I never knew it! This is nothing less than a house of God!"

Narrator: At the first hint of dawn, Jacob got up. He took the stone he had used for a pillow and set it up, as a monument to Yahweh (which was Jacob's name for God). Taking some oil from his pack, he slowly poured some over the stone, saying,

Jacob: "I name this place Bethel, the house of God."

Narrator: Then, kneeling, he vowed to himself,

Jacob: "If God goes with me and keeps me safe on this journey, if he gives me bread to eat and clothes to wear, and if I return safely to my family, then Yahweh will be my God."

Narrator: Pulling on his cloak, Jacob set off again. In time, he would meet God face to face, and God would rename him Israel, meaning "God rules." But for now, he was Jacob, moving with certainty toward his future, for he knew God would be with him.

The Story of Leah and Rachel

(Based on Genesis 29, 30:1–24, 35:16–20)

Introduction

In Genesis, the emphasis is often on God's promise made to the patriarchs Abraham, Isaac, and Jacob, who were chosen to create a people of God. Of course, the women who shared their lives often had fascinating stories themselves. Leah and Rachel, two sisters who both became Jacob's wives, led bittersweet lives, but gave to the world the twelve men who led the twelve tribes of Israel. They are the matriarchs of the House of Israel.

The following is a story to be read in two voices. You will need two readers who are comfortable in a performing role. Have them read their parts together several times before the actual reading.

The Story Begins

Leah: I am Leah, the older of two sisters, cousin of Jacob and Esau. I remember the day long ago, when Jacob came to our home. There was much excitement that day! He had left his parents, Isaac and Rebekah, and his twin brother Esau, to come live with us.

Rachel: I am Rachel, the younger sister. I too remember Jacob's arrival. He was fleeing, for he had angered his brother. He noticed me right away. He had not been with us long before I knew Jacob loved me and I him.

Leah: I could see Jacob's love for Rachel, and I was bewildered, for I knew our father Laban wanted Jacob to marry into our family, and, as the older sister, I must marry first. Who would our father choose for me so Rachel could marry Jacob? When I knew, I protested. No! This will not be a good solution! But my father never heard my protests.

Rachel (looking into the distance): Oh Jacob, my husband, the deception there has been in your life! First you deceived your father and brother, then, my father deceived you on your wedding day! **(To the audience:)** Jacob asked my father if he could marry me. My father said yes, but when it was time for the wedding, it was Leah, covered in a veil, who married Jacob. I, who loved him, stayed behind in my father's house, and cried for my loss.

Leah: What could I do? I knew Rachel was heartbroken, but what about me? I will never forget Jacob's face when the morning light came and he realized he was married to me and not to Rachel. I will never forget the shock, the disappointment, the anger...

Rachel: Jacob came to my father's house in a rage. My father calmly told him he could marry me too, if he continued to work for him. Jacob and I were married, but I must forever share my husband with my sister.

Leah: Rachel and I had always loved one another, but it was hard for me, knowing that Jacob loved her, and not me. It was a great comfort, then, when I realized I was carrying my first child.

Rachel: How happy Leah was then, and I was glad for her. But as she held her beautiful new son, Reuben, I must admit, I felt jealous.

Leah: God blessed me with sons, perhaps because I was not blessed with Jacob's love. Rachel and I had our family, wealth, food, but neither of us had what we really longed for.

Rachel: Babies, beautiful babies! My sister had Simeon, then Levi. She had more children, and I was envious. Then finally, the merciful God sent me a son! Joseph! My joy!

Leah: How Jacob doted on Joseph! It was hard on my children to see their father so taken with this new baby. But still, I was glad for Rachel. When she was carrying her second child, we began our journey.

Rachel: After all these years, Jacob wanted to return to his home and make up with his brother Esau. As we got closer to Jacob's home, Esau came to greet us.

Leah: He had forgiven Jacob. All was well, for awhile....then Rachel went into labor. I got help, for I could see it would be a difficult birth. For hours Rachel labored, I grew more and more concerned, then alarmed. I knew Rachel was slipping away from us. The child was finally born, a boy, and she said to me:

Rachel: I name him Ben-oni, son of my sorrow. Take care of him, Leah.

Leah: And then, my sister, my lifelong companion, died as I cradled her son. Our other children played outside. They would grow up and have children of their own. We would become a strong family dedicated to God. And Rachel and I, it was our love and our sacrifice that helped bring this great family into being.

The Story of Joseph

(Based on Genesis 37–46)

Introduction

Rachel's son Joseph was his father's favorite, but he was destined to leave Jacob to bring the people of Israel into Egypt, where they would further realize God's plan and love for them. Joseph's story is a complicated one for he was a prophetic man and a wise leader.

The story of Joseph and his eleven brothers is one of sibling rivalry taken to the extreme. Because this is a topic familiar to most children, this story lends itself to discussion. As you read this tale, pause along the way to explore the listeners' views of Joseph and his brothers. I have provided discussion questions at three points in the story.

The Story Begins

The older sons of Jacob were in the field, taking care of the sheep when they saw Joseph coming.

Joseph, their father's favorite. Joseph, wearing the beautiful coat their father had given him. Joseph, who had dreams in which the brothers bowed down to him. Joseph, the brother they envied, the brother they hated.

He ran up to them, glad to see them, handsome in his coat. "I had another dream last night!" he said excitedly.

That did it! They could not hear about any more bragging dreams. Two of the stronger brothers seized Joseph. Reuben, the eldest, was frightened. He was afraid they would kill Joseph.

"Throw him into that pit over there," Reuben quickly suggested, knowing he could easily rescue Joseph later. "Don't harm him." But first they took off Joseph's fine coat, and only then threw him into the pit. A caravan of merchants came along, and the brothers decided to sell Joseph as a slave to the merchants. The brothers thought, "Joseph is on his way to Egypt now. We are done with him!"

(Pause here for discussion: Why do you think Joseph's brothers were so angry with him?

Have you ever been deeply angry with a brother or sister? What do you think Joseph was feeling? What do you think happens to him?)

Joseph worked as a servant in Egypt and he began telling other people what their dreams meant. When Joseph was a young man, the Pharaoh had a dream that greatly disturbed him. He called for Joseph to interpret the dream.

"There will be seven years of plenty, when the earth will produce more food than can be eaten. This will be followed by seven years of drought, when the crops will fail, and people will starve," Joseph explained.

The Pharaoh decided to believe Joseph, and he also decided to put Joseph in charge of saving and storing the extra food, so the Egyptian people would not go hungry during the drought. Joseph was a smart man and a good leader. He did his job well, and when the seven years of plenty were over, just as Joseph predicted, the Egyptian people did not starve.

But the people in nearby countries were hungry. They heard Egypt had food and began coming there to buy some. The Pharaoh put Joseph in charge of selling the food. He was doing this job, dressed in fine Egyptian clothing and sitting in a special chair when eleven brothers came in to ask for food—eleven brothers who looked familiar!

Joseph's heart leaped for joy. Here were Reuben, Simeon, Levi, and the others. Here, too, was handsome Benjamin, his brother who had been born when their mother Rachel died. Now Benjamin was a man, and Joseph barely recognized him. He realized that none of his brothers recognized him either. There they were, bowing down to him, just as the dream had predicted years ago. Now they needed him to help them feed their families, these brothers who had sold him as a slave.

(Discussion questions: If you were Joseph, what would you do at this point? Have you ever been in a situation where you had to choose between forgiving a brother or sister or getting even?)

Joseph did not tell his brothers who he was. Instead, he gave them sacks of grain, but he instructed a servant to hide his own silver cup in Benjamin's grain. The brothers left happily with their food, but they were stopped and accused of stealing the cup. They were arrested and brought back to Joseph. Benjamin was terrified.

Now Joseph chose to explain. "I am Joseph, your brother," Joseph then told them, and he began to cry.

Amazed, bewildered, the brothers all stared at him, and of course they remembered how badly they had treated Joseph.

Still crying, Joseph told them not to be sorry. He said, "It was God's plan that I come to Egypt so I could save our family now. But tell me, is Jacob our father still alive?"

His brothers answered, "Yes."

Joseph was overjoyed! They must go home, Joseph instructed his brothers, and get their father, their wives, and children, and come back here to live with him. Joseph would see to it that they had enough food and they could all be a family once again.

It was a jubilant Jacob who traveled to Egypt with his family to join Joseph. The children, grandchildren, and great-grandchildren would all grow up there, in the land of the Pharaoh.

(Discussion questions: Joseph was no longer angry with his brothers, but still, he tricked them. What do you think of this? Joseph believed that God had wanted him to go to Egypt. Have you ever had something unusual happen in your life that later seemed to be God's plan?)

The Story of Moses and Miriam

(Based on Exodus 2:1–10, 14:15–16, 15:20–21, 16:1–3, 31:18)

Introduction

The Pharaoh of Egypt welcomed Joseph's large family with gifts, food, and land. Jacob was reunited with his son Joseph, and all led happy lives. Jacob was sometimes called Israel by God, and his family became known as the Israelites. This family grew to a tremendous size. Four hundred years passed and the family of Jacob was now a huge people living in Egypt. The memory of Joseph's great success in saving Egypt from starvation had faded, and the Pharaoh of this time was worried that the Israelites might become too powerful. So, he ordered the midwives to kill any boy children delivered to the Israelite women. And he made slaves of the people. Into this situation, the great leader Moses was born.

Moses is the central figure of the Old Testament, the great servant and mediator of God. His story is multifaceted, and, in many ways, Moses prefigures Christ. When Moses was still an infant, a ruler set out to destroy all the male Israelite children, but Moses was saved. Herod tried to kill the infant Jesus and failed. When Moses received the Ten Commandments, he had to climb to the mountaintop for this revelation. Jesus climbed a mountain for the Transfiguration. When the Israelites were led into the desert, God provided manna, a food that is often compared with the eucharist. Also, the waters of Jesus' baptism are compared to Moses' saving waters, first when he was an infant floating in a basket, and later when he parted the sea for his people to escape.

One way to engage children in this important story is through pictures. Draw simple posters of these scenes: the baby in a basket, the burning bush, parting the waters, manna in the desert, the tablets with the Ten Commandments. As you read the story, have children hold the posters, face down. When a child's scene is being described, invite him or her to come forward and hold up the poster for the rest of the class to see. If you have time, read the story in one sitting. Or read it chapter by chapter.

Chapter One: Moses Is Spared

The wind rustled in the reeds surrounding the river. Miriam sat in the tall grasses, watching and waiting.

Just a few yards away floated a basket on the water's surface. It was a fine papyrus basket, woven by her mother's able fingers, then lined, also by her mother, with bitumen and pitch. These would keep the water out, so the basket would not sink. Miriam watched it rock gently with the water's movement. She had heard stories about Noah's ark. The basket looked like she imagined the ark to look. And this basket held precious life, too, like the ark.

The silence of the morning was broken by voices. Miriam hunched smaller into the reeds and waited anxiously.

Several young women came down to the river bank to bathe. Miriam could see them now, and her heart began to pound. One of them was a princess, the Pharaoh's daughter! The very same powerful Pharaoh who held her people, the Israelite people, in slavery. The same Pharaoh who had declared that all their baby boys must be cast into the river and drowned!

And floating on this river, in the papyrus basket, lay Miriam's baby brother. Hoping to save him, her mother had placed her son into the basket to hide him by day at the river. Now he would be found by the Pharaoh's daughter! Could it be worse? If he cried, yes. There was a chance if he did not cry. Oh, please, baby, Miriam pleaded silently, don't cry!

The voices filled the air, but soon Miriam heard the sound she most dreaded: the thin, unmistakable sound of a baby's cry.

"Where is that coming from?" the Pharaoh's daughter asked, stopping her splashing and looking around.

Her attendants were silent, listening, and the baby's cries grew louder.

"It comes from over there—look there is a basket! Bring the basket to me!" the princess said.

An attendant waded into the deeper water, and drew the basket closer. The princess lifted the blanket and saw the baby. Miriam crept as close as she dared.

"Oh, this must be a child of one of the Israelites," said the Pharaoh's daughter. "It must be hungry."

Miriam knew she must act if her brother was to be saved. Perhaps the princess was not as harsh as her father, the Pharaoh. She stood up and approached the water's edge.

Gathering her courage, Miriam called, "Shall I go and find a woman who might feed the child?" Fear was betraying her voice.

Startled, the princess looked up at Miriam. Then she directed, "Yes, go."

Miriam waited to hear no more. Running, she reached her mother quickly.

When her mother, Jochebed, saw Miriam, she feared the worst. She cried out, "My baby!"

"Come, Mother! He is safe! The Pharaoh's daughter found him, and she wants a woman to take care of him!"

At the water's edge, the princess tenderly handed the crying baby to Jochebed. "Take this child and care for it until he is older. Then he can come to me," she instructed. "I will see that you are paid as long as you have him." Then she looked at the baby once more, saying, "I will name you Moses, for I saved you from the water."

Miriam, her mother, and the baby went home. As the sun rose to its height in the noon day sky, Jochebed fed her baby. Miriam knew some day her mother would have to present her little brother to the Pharaoh's daughter, and he would be raised under her care, as an Egyptian. When the baby was content, Jochebed said, "I must return to my work. Care for him, Miriam, for he is ours for a little longer."

Miriam held him close, and sang to him. He looked into her eyes as she sang.

Chapter Two: Moses Frees the Israelites

Years later, this tiny child was called by God to become a great leader. God spoke to him through a burning bush, directing him to ask the Pharaoh to set the Israelites free. But the Pharaoh was determined to keep them captive. One by one, God sent ten terrible plagues to weaken Pharaoh's resistance, but he did not relent until the tenth plague—the death of all firstborn Egyptian sons. Moses led the people of Israel out of Egypt, out of slavery. On that day hundreds of chariots and Egyptian soldiers followed them and were gaining on them. At God's direction, Moses stretched out his arm over the sea and the waters parted into two sections, leaving a path of dry land for the Israelites to escape. The waters closed back over the charioteers and they were all drowned.

Miriam herself led the people in a song and dance of celebration once they were safely across.

Chapter Three: Moses and Miriam

Miriam helped her brother as he tried to keep the people of Israel faithful to Yahweh in the long years of desert living. She heard the complaints the people hurled at Moses, for they were tired and hungry. She was there when Moses called upon God to provide food and water for the people. She ate the bread called manna that God sent.

She was there when Moses climbed a mountain where God spoke with him. God gave Moses the Ten Commandments, and God made a covenant with the Israelites. They were now God's chosen people.

Miriam was there as the people, tired of waiting for Moses to come back down the mountain, turned to false gods. She was there to see Moses' anger and pain. Together, for many years, Moses and Miriam lived amid the fears and unhappiness of the Israelites. And for all those years, they experienced God's great love and care.

Life for Miriam and Moses was difficult, but it was filled with God's presence.

Little did Miriam know of this, as she held her baby brother. She only knew that the baby was alive and safe. He would be allowed to grow up and serve God in a special way.

The house was quiet, except for Miriam's lullaby.

The Story of Ruth

(Based on the book of Ruth)

Introduction

The Israelites, over many years and with many battles, settled in Canaan, the land Moses was leading them to before his death, the land God had promised. There were times of war, times of famine, but also times of peace. In this period, Israel had no king, but there were leaders—servants of the Lord, who ruled temporarily. The book of Ruth is set during this period of history, and echoes Israel's covenant with Yahweh. Ruth and Boaz are the great-grandparents of King David.

The names of Naomi's family members may be fictitious and chosen for their symbolism: Mahlon means "sickness," Chilion means "pining away," Orpah means "she who turns away." Elimelech means "my God is king," Naomi means "my fair one," and Ruth means "the beloved."

This story is best told by a narrator, and listeners can supply Ruth's often repeated words on faithfulness.

The Story Begins

Narrator: The baby boy kicked his chubby legs and held his arms up to his grandmother. Naomi picked him up and he put his head on her shoulder. She rubbed his back and quietly sang a little chant:

Audience: Wherever you go, I shall go. Wherever you live, I shall live. Your people shall be my people, and your God shall be my God.

Narrator: As she rocked the baby to sleep, Naomi remembered how sad she had once been. Long ago, she had left this place called Bethlehem. There was a famine, and she and her family were hungry. They traveled to the land of Moab and made their home there. Her husband Elimelech died, and her two sons, Chilion and Mahlon, also died soon after marrying. Naomi, unhappy and lonely, wanted to return to her home in Bethlehem, now that the famine was over.

But first she wanted to say good-bye to her daughters-in-law. This was their homeland, where they belonged. Orpah and Ruth cried, for they both loved Naomi very much. Then Orpah said good-bye and left. Ruth, however, refused to go.

Naomi smiled as she remembered Ruth's quiet words:

Audience: Wherever you go, I shall go. Wherever you live, I shall live. Your people shall be my people, and your God shall be my God.

Narrator: Naomi had been so sad and anxious to get back home that she had simply let Ruth come with her. They traveled together, Ruth protecting and helping Naomi. When they reached Bethlehem, people there were glad to see Naomi again and interested in meeting Ruth. But still, Naomi felt unhappy and bitter about all that had happened to her. At least now they had a place to live, in Naomi's old home, but they had very little to eat.

"Is it the custom in your country that the poor may glean the leftovers from the harvest?" Ruth asked Naomi.

Naomi nodded. "If the landowner is kind."

Ruth left the house then, and Naomi watched her go, Ruth's words beginning to sink in.

Audience: Wherever you go, I shall go. Wherever you live, I shall live. Your people shall be my people, and your God shall be my God.

Narrator: Dear Ruth was going to provide food for them! Naomi, despite her sadness, turned her attention to creating a nice home for Ruth.

Ruth did the exhausting work of a gleaner. From dawn to dusk, she worked, bent over in the fields, picking barley that was left behind by the harvesters. Slowly she filled a sack with the only food that she and Naomi would have. When she returned home, her tired face shone.

"I have been met with kindness all day," Ruth said. "The owner of the field told the harvesters not to disturb me, and I think he told them to purposely leave barley behind for me!"

"Yahweh the God of Israel has been watching over you!" Naomi said.

"That is not all!" Ruth went on. "When the workers stopped to eat, the landowner called me to him. He offered me water and then he shared his bread with me! I asked him what I had done to deserve such kindness and he said—"

Ruth paused and seemed embarrassed.

"Go on," Naomi insisted.

"He said he had heard that I had left my home and everything I knew to come here with you."

Naomi was stunned. All she could think about were Ruth's words:

Audience: Wherever you go I shall go. Wherever you live, I shall live. Your people shall be my people, and your God shall be my God.

Narrator: Ruth was handing food to Naomi. "He shared so much food with me I brought you some. Please eat."

Naomi said, "Blessed be this man! Do you know his name?"

"Boaz," replied Ruth.

Naomi stared at Ruth. "Boaz? Boaz! He is a relative of my husband! He was always a kind man and generous with his great wealth. We are blessed that he has taken such a liking to you!"

And they were indeed blessed, for Boaz had seen Ruth's faithfulness to Naomi, and now he offered Ruth his own faithfulness. Eventually they were married, and of course, Naomi went to live with them.

Now the baby in her arms was asleep. Naomi gently laid him down. Someday, this beautiful child of Ruth and Boaz would have a grandson who would become the greatest king of Israel. But for today, Naomi covered the baby with a blanket and whispered:

Audience: Wherever you go, I shall go. Wherever you live, I shall live. Your people will be my people, and your God shall be my God.

The Story of Samuel

(Based on 1 Samuel 1:1–11, 3:1–20)

Introduction

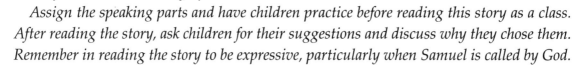

Samuel is an important figure of the Old Testament. He represents Israel's transition from a tribal confederation to a monarchy. He became the guardian of the sacred traditions, so Israel would not abandon its holy practices as it took on the ways of the world. A prophet, a priest, and the last judge, Samuel was a public figure among the twelve tribes. Like many other key characters, he began life as a longed-for child, the son of a woman who hoped and waited for years to be blessed with a child. And, when still a child, the guiding hand of Yahweh was clearly upon him.

Assign the speaking parts and have children practice before reading this story as a class. After reading the story, ask children for their suggestions and discuss why they chose them. Remember in reading the story to be expressive, particularly when Samuel is called by God.

The Story Begins

Narrator: Eli looked up to see a woman enter the temple. There were tears on her cheeks, and though she was silent, her lips moved constantly. What was her problem? Eli wondered. He peered more closely at her. She swayed a little, as she continued to mouth soundless words.

Why she must have had too much wine! As priest of this temple, Eli would have none of that here! He rose stiffly, for Eli was an old man, and walked quietly up to her.

Before he could speak, the woman turned tearful eyes on him, and she spoke.

Hannah: "Do not think ill of me. I am very unhappy, and so I pray with great sorrow. My name is Hannah, and I have no children. I am asking God to give me a son. If I could have a son, I would let the child live in the temple to serve God all his life."

Narrator: Eli nodded, then smiled kindly.

Eli: "Go in peace. May the God of Israel grant you what you have asked."

Narrator: The woman, Hannah, left the temple quietly. Sometime later, God answered her prayer. She and her husband became parents of a son, Samuel, which means "called by God." When Samuel was old enough, Hannah carried out her promise: she took him to the temple, where he stayed to live with Eli, serving God.

One night, the child Samuel went to sleep as usual. Eli was also asleep. All was quiet. Samuel rolled over. He opened his eyes. Why had he awakened? There was no sound, nothing was amiss. Samuel yawned and closed his eyes.

God: "Samuel!"

Narrator: Samuel sat up. Eli must need something.

Samuel: "Here I am!"

Narrator: Jumping up, and running to Eli's bed, he said,

Samuel: "Here I am. Do you need something?"

Narrator: Eli opened one eye just enough to see Samuel standing there, looking very drowsy.

Eli: "I did not call you. Go back to sleep."

Narrator: Samuel walked back to his bed, and thought that he must have been dreaming. It had seemed so real! But, soon, the boy was settled down again, and slumbering soundly.

God: "Samuel!"

Narrator: Wearily, Samuel got up and stumbled into Eli's room.

Samuel: "Here I am. You called me."

Narrator: More awake now, Eli answered,

Eli: "I did not call you, my son. Go back to sleep."

Narrator: Puzzled, Samuel lay down, but soon the voice again called him. Once more, he stumbled off to Eli's room. By this time, Eli was sitting up, unable to sleep. He had not heard any voice, but he knew that Samuel was not dreaming. Eli knew that God was calling the boy.

Eli: "Go to sleep, and if you are called again, reply, 'Speak, Lord, for your servant is listening.'"

Narrator: Once more, Samuel lay down, but soon he awoke to the voice,

God: "Samuel, Samuel!"

Samuel: "Speak, Lord, for your servant is listening,"

Narrator: And God began speaking to Samuel. From that day on, God spoke to Samuel. Samuel told others what God said. Samuel became a great prophet, and served God all his life.

The Story of David

(based on 1 Samuel 16, 17:1–50, and Psalm 23)

Introduction

One of Jesus' most celebrated ancestors was King David. Chosen by God to become king and anointed by the prophet Samuel, David led a remarkable life. His abilities as a warrior and political leader were tremendous. He was a wise and caring king. Often hounded by controversy and heady with power, David made mistakes too, but he looked for God's forgiveness and began again. It is in his music and poetry that the depth of David's soul is revealed to us. In the psalms, we see his struggles and his immeasurable faith in God. While it is uncertain how many he actually wrote, many are attributed to him because he was held in such great esteem. Because of David and other musicians, we too can find God through the poetry of the Old Testament.

Psalm 23 has been set to music in a variety of ways. Find a version your listeners may be familiar with and sing it together when David sings it in this story. If you don't have a sung version, simply have children chant the sung response each time it appears.

The Story Begins

It began as a quiet day. The puffy clouds drifted by, the sheep grazed lazily. Young David the shepherd looked around, but he sensed no danger from wild animals. His sling and stones were always ready, however. More than once he had killed a bear or lion who had come bounding out of the thicket to steal sheep. One shot from David's sling, and the fierce animal lay dead. But not today. It was a quiet day.

The wind rustled the grasses, a few sheep bleated. David picked up his harp and began to sing. His clear, sweet voice took up a song of his own words. David was a poet and musician as well as a shepherd. Then, over the wind, David heard a shout. Running toward him was a servant of his father, Jesse. David stood and the man dashed up, almost too breathless to speak. "Your father sends for you," he said, gasping. "I am to stay with the sheep. Go now."

"Is something wrong with my father?"

"No, it is someone else who asks for you. A great man. People in town say he is a seer, a prophet! His name is Samuel. He came to your father's house, saying the Lord had sent him! He said he is to choose the next king from among Jesse's sons!"

David picked up his harp, marveling at these words. The next king? But what of King Saul? Wouldn't he be king for a long time yet?

"Why choose a king from amongst my brothers?" David wondered aloud. "What does he know of us? And if he does choose, it would be Eliab, the eldest. Why must I go?"

"This Samuel says it is not he who chooses, but the Lord. And he insists he must see all of Jesse's sons. Hurry now. They are waiting for you!"

Sung Refrain: My shepherd is the Lord, nothing indeed shall I want.

David left the field, a handsome lad with clear, understanding eyes and a confident walk. He entered his house and found his entire family and the prophet Samuel waiting for him near the table, which had been set with dinner.

His father, Jesse, approached David and said to Samuel, "This is my youngest son, David."

David looked upon Samuel, an old man. Samuel could see in David's eyes the trust David had for God. Closing his own eyes, Samuel remained silent for a moment. Then, he opened his eyes and took a horn filled with precious oil from his belt. He walked up to David and anointed him with the special oil. "Someday, you will be a great king, perhaps the greatest king, for Yahweh has chosen you," Samuel said.

It was still a quiet day. His family whom he knew so well stood with him. The house had not changed. But for David, nothing would ever be the same again. He was filled with the spirit of the Lord Yahweh, and this spirit would stay with him for the rest of his life. He wore no crown, but he had been anointed with holy oil, and no one could remove it. Once a king, always a king.

Sung Refrain: My shepherd is the Lord, nothing indeed shall I want.

There were many changes ahead for David. The present king, Saul, was a troubled man who no longer trusted in Yahweh. Often, he would become so sad and depressed he was unable to go on with his work. His servants suggested that music might help. One said he had heard that a son of Jesse was a skilled harpist whose music was said to soothe many.

So David was welcomed to the palace and he spent hours playing his harp and singing his poetry to the king. Saul sat motionless, his eyes downcast. David, his fingers picking out a delicate tune on the harp, sang,

Sung Refrain: My shepherd is the Lord, nothing indeed shall I want.

The king looked up, much soothed. There was love in his eyes for the young David. Soon the servants said that David the musician was a healer, too.

David next discovered the warrior in himself. King Saul's army, in which some of David's brothers were soldiers, was fighting the Philistines. One day, David took food to his brothers. There he saw a frightening scene: in the Philistine army was a huge man, a giant of a man named Goliath, who taunted the Israelites every morning and every night.

David saw that Goliath was enormous. He was much taller than the tallest man of the Israelites. His shoulders were broader than any others, his arms and legs were like tree trunks. His massive armor glinted in the sun, and he roared at Saul's men, "Why must we fight a war? Let one man come forward to fight me! If he kills me, we will be your slaves. If I kill your soldier, you will be our slaves!" And then he laughed, a terrible laugh.

David, still a boy, took out his sling. Had he not killed lions? Had he not killed bears? Would Yahweh not protect him as he slew this bear of a man? The boy approached the giant.

Goliath laughed again. "Am I a dog that you come to me with sticks?"

But David, with five smooth stones in his pouch, ran toward the towering enemy. As if a lion were about to devour his sheep, David fitted a stone into his sling. It whizzed through the air and hit Goliath in the forehead. The huge man crumbled to the ground, dead.

After that, David became part of the army, and soon the soldiers said that David was a good warrior.

Sung Refrain: My shepherd is the Lord, nothing indeed shall I want.

David continued to sing for the king, and then he began his life as a leader of soldiers. Someday he would become a celebrated warrior, and he would write and sing more songs. Then, he would become the exalted King David. King David would unite the people of Israel into a great nation. During his reign, he would do what he thought was right, but sometimes he would make mistakes. Always he would trust in God. He would ask for forgiveness, he would ask for guidance. Yes, he would become a king who would be remembered for all time, but he would also remain a faithful servant of Yahweh, his God.

Sung Refrain: My shepherd is the Lord, nothing indeed shall I want.

The Story of Solomon

(based on 1 Kings 3:4–28, 5:9, 6, 7, 10:1–13)

Introduction

Jesus was born a child of poverty and powerlessness, but centuries before his birth, his ancestor, King Solomon, possessed tremendous wealth and power. Solomon, David's son, reigned in a time of peace, and he was able to have constructed the magnificent temple that David had hoped to build. But Solomon is most revered for his wisdom, his understanding heart. Solomon's story is a story of God's blessings, for everything that he is remembered for were gifts from Yahweh.

After reading this story (which requires ten readers), have a discussion about wisdom. Do children know what wisdom is? Do they know any "wise" people in this day and age? Then have children role play the story of the two women fighting over a baby. What do they think of Solomon's decision?

The Story Begins

Reader One: Because she was queen, she had met many powerful people. She had known many who were wealthy, like she was. Because of her position, she had sought out those who were wise, too. But it was the stories of King Solomon of Israel that most intrigued her. Some said he was more powerful than other kings. Others said he was the most wealthy king to ever live. Still others talked of his incredible wisdom. She, the Queen of Sheba of Arabia, wanted to meet this man. She was on her way there now.

Reader Two: The Queen was very aware that she held a position of great honor, too. Hers was not a time when women held power. Even those born into royal families had little to say of their own futures, much less the futures of their countries. But she was the queen, the one who ruled, the one who must be wise. Now she sought out the man whose wisdom had become legendary. His wealth and power interested her, but it was his wisdom that she most wanted to witness. She kept thinking of the stories she had heard, and one in particular haunted her.

Reader Three: Two women came to Solomon, the story tells, with a newborn baby. Each claimed the child was hers.

"We each had newly born sons, my Lord," the first woman explained. "In the night, hers died. She woke, saw her baby was dead, and took my living child. She put the dead baby next to me as I slept. In the morning, I awoke and saw the baby was dead, and then realized he wasn't my baby. This child is mine!"

"She lies!" the second woman insisted. "The live child is mine!"

"No, no! He is my child!" the first persisted.

They continued to argue before the king.

Reader Four: King Solomon listened. Then he said, "Bring me a sword."

A silence fell upon the room as a sword was brought. "Cut the living child in two and give half to each woman," the king calmly said.

"My Lord, please do not harm the child! Give him to her, but please, do not kill the baby!" cried the first woman.

"He shall belong to neither of us," the second woman said. "Divide him."

Then King Solomon spoke, "Give the child to the first woman. Do not kill him. She is his mother."

Reader Five: The Queen of Sheba thought of this story as she traveled closer to Israel. It was said that Solomon had a heart as vast as the sand on the seashore. That was a man she wanted to meet. She heard, too, that Solomon had written more than a thousand songs. He could speak knowledgeably of trees and plant life. He knew much about birds, reptiles, fish, and other animals. And his wise sayings particularly fascinated her:

Reader Six: "Better a dinner of vegetables where love is than a fatted ox and hatred with it." "The mouths of fools are their ruin, and their lips a snare to themselves." "When you make a vow to God, do not delay fulfilling it; for God has no pleasure in fools. Fulfill what you vow."

The Queen now wondered about King Solomon's God. She had heard that all this wisdom, power, and wealth were bestowed upon Solomon by God. Long ago, when he had just become king, he had been visited by his God in a dream. God had asked the young Solomon what he wanted.

Reader Seven: "Yahweh, my God, I am unskilled in leadership, yet you have made me king of this people of yours, a people so vast they cannot be counted. Please give me, your servant, an understanding heart, so I can decide between good and evil," Solomon had answered.

God had been pleased. "Since you have asked for this and not for riches or a long life, I will give you a heart wise and shrewd as none before you has had and none will have after you. I will also give you what you have not asked for: you will have riches greater than any other king, and a long life."

Reader Eight: Solomon then awoke and praised God, offering thanksgiving.

All that the dream had predicted had come true, the Queen had heard. Now, she traveled to see for herself.

She did not come empty-handed. She and her servants traveled with camels loaded with costly spices, great quantities of gold, and precious stones. She was bringing King Solomon gifts, but she came to question him.

The Queen of Sheba arrived in Jerusalem. She admired the temple that Solomon had built, the temple where he worshiped. It was constructed with the finest of wood, the best of stone. Fragrant cedar wood was carved into roses, olive wood angel statues looked upon worshipers, and gold covered the inside of the temple. A golden altar and table were some of the furnishings.

Reader Nine: In the streets the queen saw a thousand chariots and thousands of horses. She saw ivory, gold, jewels, armor, spices, and exquisite fabrics all around her. She saw the fleet of ships he owned. Then she saw the palace, with its ornate bronze pillars, filled with well-dressed, well-fed servants. The Queen of Sheba was stunned. Even she had never seen so much wealth.

She went to Solomon, arrayed in her own glory and wealth. He received her graciously, as he did all the royal visitors who brought him gifts. The Queen of Sheba would give him her gifts, but first, there was something more important.

The Queen began questioning the King. Question after question, one more difficult than the next, she questioned him. And King Solomon answered them, one by one, carefully, correctly, wisely. Finally, her questions stopped.

Reader Ten: She said, "What I heard about you in my own country was true! Until I came and saw it with my own eyes, I could not believe what they told me, yet they told me less than half. For wisdom and prosperity you surpass the report I heard. How happy your family and servants must be! I know it is because of your God that you possess so much, in all ways. Blessed be Yahweh, your God who has granted you his favor! Because of your God's love for this people, you are able to deal with law and justice."

Then she gave him one hundred and twenty talents of gold, precious stones, and a wealth of spices, more than was ever given to King Solomon. He in turn gave her many gifts from his bounty. And she returned home.

The Story of Elijah

(based on 1 Kings 17:1–24, 18:20–46, 2 Kings 2:1–13)

Introduction

The great prophet Elijah ministered during the years 874-852 B.C. He came from the desert highlands of Gilead during a time when Israel's leaders were choosing false gods over Yahweh. But Elijah's name means "My God-Yahweh" and he was not going to sit idly by as his country turned away from God. He performed miracles and preached, predicting the downfall of Israel. Elijah was so influential that he is mentioned many times in the New Testament in relation to Jesus. During Christ's public years, some people thought him to be Elijah, who was expected to return. In the Transfiguration on Mt. Tabor, it was Elijah, along with Moses, who appeared with Jesus.

It is a Jewish custom at the Seder meal served during Passover to hope for the arrival of the prophet Elijah. He will bring a time of great peace and harmony, when evil will be vanquished forever. In honor of Elijah, a large and beautiful wine cup is set for him at the Seder table, and the door is left ajar in hope that he will come. Before reading this story, arrange a placemat, a plate, a glass filled with water, and silverware carefully and deliberately before your listeners. If possible, open the door. Do not explain your actions, simply ask your audience to listen to the story and see why you have done this. After reading the story, ask listeners what they think of the woman's belief that Elijah would return. Is there a Christian belief similar to this one? For whom do we set the table and open the door?

The Story Begins

So that is what happened to the holy man, the widow in Zarephath thought after she had heard the news. She sat quietly and reflected on all that had happened. Amazing as this news was, it did not surprise her. It was right, she knew.

Her son, now a strong boy in his teens, came in.

"Do you remember Elijah?" she asked.

"How can I ever forget him? He saved my life!" was her son's response.

"He did not just save it—he got it back for you," she said.

"He saved me twice. Do you remember how we were starving before he came?" the boy said. "We had no more food and you thought we would soon die."

She nodded, more at the memory than at her son. "I was desperate. The drought had gone on so long, and I had no way of feeding you. I was gathering sticks for one last fire to make the last bread before we died. And when I looked up, there stood Elijah. He wore a goatskin cloak, and his hair was long. He asked me to bring him some water, and as I turned to do so, he called after me, asking for some bread. I could tell he was an Israelite, so I answered, 'As Yahweh your God lives, I have no baked bread, only a handful of meal and a bit of oil left. My son and I will soon die.' I will never forget what he replied."

The son remained silent, waiting for his mother's memories.

"'Do not be afraid. Go and make some bread for yourself and your son and for me also. For the God of Israel says, "Jar of meal shall not be spent, jug of oil shall not be emptied, before the day when Yahweh sends rain on the face of the earth."' And we never ran out of food!"

Her son nodded. "Because of him, we had food—he saved me then. He stayed with us for quite a while. I asked him how he had eaten before he came to us and he said the ravens brought him food—bread every morning, meat every night! I loved hearing that, but I didn't believe him."

"Oh, I have no doubt that what he said was true. What is that compared to raising you back to life?"

A faraway look came over the son's face.

The mother spoke, "I will never, never forget that day. You fell ill. I was terrified that I would lose you, too, as I had lost your father, but I could not save you. Elijah came in just as you had died. I was holding you and weeping. Elijah took you into his arms, took your body up to the upper room and laid you down on the bed. I heard his loud voice calling, 'Yahweh my God, may the breath of life, I beg you, come into this child again!' Though I was filled with grief and despair, those words, that voice, seemed to go right through me."

Her son remembered, "I sat up then, I remember, and he took me back downstairs to you. I didn't understand what happened."

There were tears in the mother's eyes now. "You were alive! I can still see him, climbing down, and you—alive! awake!—in his arms! At that moment, I truly knew that Elijah was a man of God."

"When he left here, he proved that to many others, too. He fought so hard against the king and queen's belief in the false god, Baal. Oh, how I wish I had been there when he challenged the prophets of Baal to sacrifice a bull to Baal, and have Baal himself light the fire!"

She laughed. "I heard they prayed and cried and begged all morning and all afternoon, but their god never responded."

"But Elijah waited patiently, and then he repaired the altar to Yahweh, putting twelve stones around it for the twelve sons of Jacob. Then he poured water—precious water in that drought!—all over the altar and wood, so it would be impossible to light. Then Elijah prayed—-"

"He was a prayerful man, and it was thrilling to hear him call upon God!" the mother exclaimed.

"Elijah asked Yahweh to send a fire, so the people there would again believe in Yahweh, and not in false gods. And the fire rained down, burning that soaked wood. Then, the people fell to the ground, in awe of Yahweh. Later, Elijah killed all the prophets of Baal. And the drought ended then, too, because Yahweh wanted it to."

"But Mother, what made you think of him today? Has something happened?"

She nodded. "I have heard that Elijah is gone..."

"He died?"

She smiled. "Well no, but I heard he has chosen a successor, a man named Elisha. They traveled to Bethel, then to Jericho, then on to the river Jordan. When they reached the river, Elijah struck the waters with his cloak..."

"That cloak!" the son said, amused.

"And the waters divided, just as they did for Moses! The two crossed, and Elisha told others later that a chariot appeared—just appeared. It was made of fire, pulled by horses also made of fire! It came nearer until it stood between them. Then, Elijah was taken up to heaven in a whirlwind!"

The mother finished her story, and both remained silent, awed.

Then she stood up, looking up toward the room where Elijah had once slept, and had once brought her son back to life.

"He truly was a man of God," she said quietly, reverently.

Her son stood beside her. "He will be back," he said. "Elijah will return."

The Story of Isaiah

(based on Isaiah 6:1–13, 9:1, 5–6)

Introduction

In the years after the death of Solomon, the kingdom of Israel, once so strong under the leadership of King David, broke up. Ten of the tribes, called Israel, went north, and made their capital Shechem. The remaining two, Judah and Benjamin, united and became known as the tribe of Judah, whose capital was Jerusalem. Internal strife set in and worshiping false gods continued (as in the story of Elijah).

A nation called Assyria rose swiftly to power and overran the ten tribes. They scattered the vanquished Israelites so they could not reunite. That is the last of what is known of those ten tribes.

Many years later, the Babylonians captured Judah, claiming the Holy Land and destroying the city of Jerusalem. The conquered tribe of Judah was led into captivity in Babylon, where their name was changed to Jews, from the Hebrew word "Yehudi," meaning "belonging to the tribe of Judah." It was prior to this exile in Babylon that Elijah worked, and another voice was heard at this time: that of Isaiah. Isaiah, a statesman who worked with the king, warned and predicted this downfall of Judah, but his warning fell on deaf ears. After the capture and exile to Babylon, Isaiah's followers continued to prophesy. It was through Isaiah that the coming of Jesus was foretold.

Practice the refrain before reading the story and assign readers to be the voices of Isaiah, the Seraph, and God.

The Story Begins

Narrator: Isaiah was not a poor man. He was well-educated, and often worked for the king. He had a gift for understanding the ways that governments worked. He understood how wars started, and he wanted to avoid them. Often the king called upon him for advice.

But Isaiah loved and believed in a much higher king. He was a follower of Yahweh. One day, he was called upon by God—through a vision!

He saw the Lord sitting on a throne, high and lofty. The hem of God's robe filled the temple! Attending God were seraphs, a kind of angel. Each had six wings: with two they covered their faces, and with two they covered their feet, and with two they flew. The seraphs called to one another.

Chorus: Holy, holy, holy is the Lord! God's glory fills the whole earth!

Narrator: Isaiah felt the foundations of the doorways shake as they cried out, and the temple was filled with smoke. He said:

Isaiah: "How unhappy I am! I am lost, for I am a man of unclean, sinful lips, and I live among a sinful people, a people of unclean lips. Yet, my eyes have looked at the King, Yahweh!"

Narrator: After he said that, one the of seraphs flew to him, holding a live coal taken from the altar with a pair of tongs. The seraph touched Isaiah's lips with the coal and said:

Seraph: "Now that this has touched your lips, you are cleansed, your guilt has departed, and your sin is blotted out."

Narrator: Then Isaiah heard the voice of God saying:

God: "Whom shall I send? Who will be our messenger?"

And Isaiah called out:

Isaiah: "Here I am. Send me!"

Chorus: Holy, holy, holy is the Lord! God's glory fills the whole earth!

Narrator: So, Isaiah became a great prophet, the voice of God. He advised the king, he advised the people. He prophesied the coming destruction of their country; he scolded people for living badly. His words were filled with wisdom, with hope for God's great love. The people of his time did not listen, but later people would read the words of Isaiah, and take them to heart.

It was Isaiah's voice that foretold the greatest event: the coming of the Messiah, the Savior, who would be Jesus. Isaiah was on the far side of the Jordan River when he prophesied:

Isaiah: "The people that walked in darkness have seen a great light; on those who live in a land of deep shadow a light has shone.

For there is a child born for us, a son given us, and dominion is laid on his shoulders, and this is the name they give him: Wonder Counselor, Mighty God, Eternal Father, Prince of Peace."

Chorus: Holy, holy, holy is the Lord! God's glory fills the whole earth!

The Story of Nehemiah

(based on Nehemiah 1, 2, 3, 4, 7:1, 12:27–43)

Introduction

The Jews' time of exile in Babylon was unlike their ancestors' enslavement in Egypt of Moses' time. In Babylon, they were assimilated into Babylonian culture, and there was great danger of losing their identity as Jews, of losing sight of the true God, of lapsing into the comfortable ways of the Babylonians.

Then, Persia defeated the Babylonians. King Cyrus of Persia permitted the Jews to leave Babylon and return to Jerusalem and the surrounding land. The Jews went back in waves, nothing like the frantic exodus out of Egypt. Back in the Promised Land, they faced both a devastated city and a damaged identity. It was these conditions under which Nehemiah began his work.

Nehemiah reconstructed the wall surrounding Jerusalem, and he tried to rebuild the integrity of the Jews by drawing on the strength and abilities of the community. In Scripture, Nehemiah told his own story. He will do so here, too.

Divide the listeners into two groups, the Nehemiah chorus and the Sanballat chorus, to read the lines assigned to each. When using this with younger children, you may want to end the story with the two groups being the celebratory choirs. They can march separately around the sides of the room and meet in the center for a song of praise and thanksgiving.

The Story Begins

I am Nehemiah, son of Hacaliah. I was living in Babylon, and I was cupbearer to the king. King Artaxerxes was a good man, and I was on very good terms with him.

I was also a devout Jew, living far away from the holy city of Jerusalem. Often I asked travelers how my fellow Jews were faring, the ones who had returned to Jerusalem sometime ago after our many years of exile in Babylon. What I heard left me deeply saddened.

My friend Hanani told me, "Those who are back home are in great trouble. The protective walls surrounding Jerusalem are in ruins and the gates burned down. Over the years, several armies have swept through and there is rubble everywhere. In fact, that is what the people are using to rebuild! Their houses are made of the debris from the ruined city. When they were allowed to leave Babylon, they went back with such high hopes. But they are in despair now."

I wept when I heard this. I cried out to Yahweh, my God. I asked God to help me help my people. My sadness was so great, the king noticed and asked me if I was ill. Respectfully, I told him of the despair of my people. That good king then asked me what I wanted.

Silently I called upon the God of heaven to help me. Then I said aloud, "If it pleases the king, I ask for leave to go to the land of my ancestors, to help rebuild it."

The king not only gave me permission to leave for an extended time, he gave me letters granting me power and the authority to govern when I got there, as well as lumber to help with the building. The king was kind to me, because God was with me.

Traveling toward my homeland, I showed my papers, the ones granting me the right to be governor, to other leaders along the way so they would let me pass through their lands. When the governor of nearby Samaria, Sanballat by name, heard of my power and of my mission, he was very angry. He did not want anyone to help the children of Israel. I felt sure that he would make trouble for me.

Sanballat Chorus: Nehemiah, go back to Babylon. Leave Jerusalem alone!

When I reached Jerusalem, I did not make myself known to anyone at first. Instead I made camp, and at night I rose and made my way around the ruined wall, inspecting and planning. The devastation was bad and the work ahead of us would be enormous. But I did not despair, for God was with us. For three nights I made my rounds unseen and no one knew what my plan was. Then I called a meeting. Everyone came: the high priest, the goldsmiths, the homeowners. There was a crowd and I spoke:

"You see the trouble we are in: Jerusalem is in ruins, and we have no wall to protect us. Even the gates have been burned. Come, let us rebuild the walls. Let us give ourselves protection once again. Let us give Jerusalem the dignity this great city deserves!"

Then I told them of God's favor that I knew was upon us, and of the king's support. They listened, but they knew the task ahead was an overwhelming one. I went on, "This job is too big for any one group. It will take all of us, working together to complete it. I will organize small groups, and each will take a section. Work hard on your section, make it sound. Put your pride into it, for your work will contribute to the whole. Your section will make our city strong once again."

Their response was great.

Nehemiah Chorus: "Let's build! Let's begin! Let us be strong once again!"

They began immediately, bringing tools, getting lumber. I organized work crews, choosing who truly believed in our project. Anyone could work, their skills did not matter. What mattered was that they cared about the city. I traveled about, seeing that each section would be repaired, making certain there were enough workers in each place.

Eliashib, the high priest, and the other priests rebuilt the Sheep Gate, Uzziel of the goldsmiths' guild worked next to Hananiah of the perfumers' guild. Rephanian, ruler of half a district of Jerusalem, came to work. Some people carried out repairs in front of their own houses.

Of course, Sanballat came with some others to ridicule. They found me as I worked with Hananiah. They called to us, sneers on their faces.

Sanballat Chorus: What are you doing? Are you planning to revolt against the king?

Then they laughed mockingly at us.

Hananiah and his workers silently kept at their tasks, but I called back calmly, "The God of heaven will give us success. We, God's servants, are going to build!"

And we did. Little by little, the wall was being rebuilt. And, little by little, the good Jewish folk working were feeling better and better.

Nehemiah Chorus: There is hope! Our city will be strong again. We will succeed!

Sanballat went into a rage when he heard of our progress. He came by again to ridicule the workers. He spoke of our work to others,

Sanballat Chorus: What are you pathetic people trying to do? Do you expect to finish in one day? Do you think you can put new life into these charred stones?

He was not content just to jeer; he began to plot. I learned he was gathering a group to attack us. Quickly, I called a meeting. "God is with us," I reminded the workers. "We will set up a watch, day and night."

Nehemiah Chorus: We still have much work to do! And now there are threats to our safety! We will never finish!

That was followed by murmurs that became shouts of agreement. They were losing heart and fear was taking over, just as Sanballat hoped.

I said to them: "Do not be afraid. Keep your minds on the Lord! Each family must post guards, armed with swords, spears, and bows. We will not let them stop us!"

That is what happened. We organized and our enemies, learning that God had thwarted their plan, withdrew.

The work went on, the hope and pride renewed. But from that day on, only half the people worked. The other half stood with them, armed with spears, shields, breastplates, bows. Even the workers were armed. I had a trumpeter ready, to sound an alarm if needed.

We worked, from the break of day until the stars appeared, and always we kept watch, night and day. In fifty-two days, the wall was completed, for the hearts of the people were in their work, and God was with us.

Of course, we held a ceremony to dedicate the wall. The people of Jerusalem joined into two choirs and marched along the top of the wall, one to the right, the other to the left. They played trumpets, harps, cymbals, and lutes, coming together at the temple. The music carried us joyfully for hours. The jubilation of Jerusalem was heard for miles around.

The Story of Jonah

(based on the book of Jonah)

Introduction

The prophet Jonah ben Amittai was a historical figure who lived about seven hundred years after the renowned kings David and Solomon. There is great debate about this story. The author was not Jonah himself, but used Jonah's revered name to give credit to his story. Some say it is reliable history, while others say it is a wonderful parable. Christians may see Jonah as prefiguring Christ, for as Saint Matthew observed, Jonah spent three days in the belly of the fish as Christ spent three days in the heart of the earth. Moslems call him "Yunus" and some claim there is a mosque that holds his tomb and a tooth from the fish that swallowed him. The Jews read his story each year in observance of the sacred Day of Atonement, because it is a story of God's great mercy and compassion for those who seek repentance and forgiveness.

The book of Jonah leaves us with a challenge. It ends with a question, a question from God. We do not learn of Jonah's answer. Perhaps that is so the readers of each generation will seek to answer it for themselves. Because this story is long, assign readers and practice with them beforehand.

The Story Begins

Narrator: Jonah was a prophet. It was not an easy job, and some days were harder than others. But this, this was the worst day of all!

Yahweh had directed him to preach to the people of Nineveh—Nineveh! Jonah had heard about that great city: it was so large that the wall surrounding it was eight miles long! The wall was one hundred feet high! And inside that wall was a city so vast, so rich, that there were fifteen hundred towers on buildings, temples to many gods, and water was brought in from thirty miles away!

What's more, they were unbelievers there, not followers of Yahweh. And he, Jonah, was to travel to Nineveh and tell those pagan people that Yahweh was unhappy with them? If anyone at all listened to him, they would laugh him out of town. Or throw him out.

Reader One: Jonah set his chin stubbornly. God must plan to be merciful to the citizens of Nineveh, those wicked people. Why should he, Jonah, help them? They didn't deserve to be saved! Besides, it was over five hundred miles to Nineveh…

Reader Two: He wasn't going to do it. Jonah decided to flee in the opposite direction. He went to the seaport town of Joppa and found a ship bound for Tarshish, a place so far away it was called "the end of the world." Oh, what a relief he felt as he boarded the ship! He'd never get to Nineveh now. Jonah was so relaxed, he went down into the hold and fell asleep.

Reader Three: While Jonah was sleeping, Yahweh sent a great wind upon the sea. A storm rose up, and soon the sailors feared the ship would be destroyed and they would all drown. Throwing cargo overboard to lighten their load, the sailors all cried out to their various gods, begging to be saved. When they found Jonah was asleep, they shouted to him to pray to his God. Then they decided if they cast lots, the one who lost was the one who was causing the storm. Jonah lost.

Reader Four: Desperately, one sailor asked him, "What is your business? Where do you come from?"

"I am Hebrew. I worship Yahweh, the God of heaven and earth," Jonah answered. "I am causing the storm, I'm sure. Throw me overboard, and the sea will grow calm. I do not want you to suffer because of me."

Narrator: The sailors did not want to do this. Instead, they rowed hard, trying to reach shore, but the storm only grew worse. Finally, they prayed to Jonah's God, asking God to understand that they were doing what they thought God wanted. Then, they threw Jonah overboard. Immediately, the waters grew calm, and the sailors trembled in fear.

Jonah plunged down, down, down into the sea. He knew it was the end. He should have gone to Nineveh. But suddenly a dark shadow passed in front of him and in the murky waters he realized it was the huge open jaws of a great fish. God had arranged that the fish swallow him. Before Jonah could struggle, he was in the belly of the fish!

Reader Five: At first Jonah was relieved. He could breathe here! He would not drown. Then he looked around. Seaweed, small fish, bones floated around him. Bones. How long would it be before those bones included his? It was dark, it smelled. Would he starve first, or be digested?

Reader Six: Water surrounded him up to his throat, seaweed wrapped around his head. And Jonah despaired. He cried out to Yahweh. He was deeply sorry for not having gone to Nineveh. Would God please forgive him and give him another chance? For three days and three nights, Jonah waited and prayed in the belly of the fish.

Reader Seven: Yahweh spoke to the fish, and the fish spat Jonah onto the shore. He landed on the sand. He blinked in the daylight. He breathed in deeply the fresh air. He untangled the seaweed from his fingers and hair. He shivered, then felt the warm sunlight on his skin. It was so good to be alive!

Then he heard God's voice. "Up, Jonah. Go to Nineveh. Preach to the people there as I have told you."

Reader Eight: This time Jonah went. He arrived at the wickedly beautiful city several days later. Jonah saw its richness and sighed with despair. What was the point? Why would anyone here believe him? Even if some did, Jonah thought bitterly, they did not deserve God's love. Still, he had to try. He dragged himself around all day, talking to people alone or standing on steps and preaching.

"Only forty more days and Nineveh will be destroyed!" he shouted.

Narrator: Much to Jonah's amazement, the people listened. They told Jonah that they would fast and wear sackcloth (rough clothing), to show that they were sorry. News of this reached the king. He rose from his throne, took off his royal robes, and dressed in sackcloth. He proclaimed to the whole city, "People and all animals are to eat nothing or drink water for three days. All must call upon God, saying we will change our evil ways!"

And the people and animals of Nineveh fasted and prayed. God heard their prayers and had mercy on them. No disaster destroyed their city.

Reader Nine: Jonah was furious. His prayers were angry ones. "Isn't this what I said would happen when I was still at home? That's why I fled to Tarshish. I knew you were a God of tenderness and compassion. I knew you would be slow to anger, that you would relent!" Jonah was so disgusted, he added, "So now, Yahweh, please take my life away."

Reader Ten: Yahweh said simply, "Are you right to be this angry?" Jonah then left the city going east. Some distance away, so he could see the city, Jonah made himself a shelter. He was still angry. God provided a vine to soothe him. It grew up over Jonah's shelter and Jonah delighted in it. At dawn, God sent a worm to attack the vine, so it withered. When the sun had risen, God sent a scorching wind. Jonah was so overcome with heat and misery, he called out to God, begging for death.

Narrator: Yahweh asked, "Are you right to be so angry about the plant?" Jonah replied crossly, "I have every right to be angry, to the point of death!"

"You feel pity for the vine, which you did not plant or tend. It lived only one day. So should I not feel pity for Nineveh, for the one hundred and twenty thousand people who do not know right from wrong, to say nothing of the animals?"

Jonah was silent. For once he did not know how to answer.

The Story of Esther

(Based on the book of Esther)

Introduction

The book of Esther is one of only three books in the Old Testament bearing the name of a woman in its title. Its setting is a sumptuous palace in the Persian Empire, between the fifth and fourth century. The book is among the historical stories written in a literary form. It is filled with plots and counter-plots, and is skillfully composed. The author lived about 130 B.C., at a time when the Jews had had some successes in throwing off the power of other rulers, but there was always the fear of conquest. Consequently, all Jews needed to be encouraged to fight and even risk death for their country. The story of Esther is just that kind of encouragement. Her bravery, intelligence, and insight still inspire each year in Jewish synagogues when her story is read at the Feast of Purim.

This version can be read by one reader, omitting the refrain, or it can be read in parts, with a narrator and a reader for Esther's part, with the audience adding the refrain.

The Story Begins

Narrator: Esther was a young Jewish woman living in the country of Persia when Ahasuerus was king. When the king was to marry, he wanted a queen of great beauty. He called for the most beautiful women in the country to come to his palace, and from this group, he chose Esther. Before going to live in the palace, she said good-bye to her cousin Mordecai who had raised her after her parents died.

Mordecai advised her, "Esther, tell no one that you are Jewish, for there are always those who are against us. Go now, but know that I will not be far away. May God be with you."

Refrain: Esther, Esther, you must save your people!

Narrator: King Ahasuerus was a mighty ruler and he had a large country to govern. He had many helpers to keep his kingdom in order. The one who held the most power was Haman. Now Haman loved this power, and he ordered all people to bow down to him. Everyone did, except one man: Mordecai.

Concerned for Esther, Mordecai now lived near the palace. Haman passed by him each day, and always Mordecai refused to bow, for he believed that he should bow before God alone. As a devout Jew, Mordecai chose to risk angering Haman rather than displease God.

Haman did indeed become angry, so angry he wanted to see Mordecai dead. Each day, his anger grew until he wanted to kill not only Mordecai, but all Jews, for they shared Mordecai's religion.

Refrain: Esther, Esther, you must save your people!

Narrator: Haman went to the king. He said, "Your majesty, in your country there is a certain group of people living apart, with laws differing from those of every other people. They do not obey the laws of the king. Shall we have them killed?"

Haman did not say who these people were, or how they behaved, and the king did not ask.

"Do with them whatever you please," said the king. Neither he nor Haman realized they had just condemned the queen to die.

Haman arranged that on the thirteenth day of the twelfth month, all the Jews in the entire country of Persia would be killed. A decree declaring this was sent out to all the governors in the kingdom.

Refrain: Esther, Esther, you must save your people!

Narrator: Everywhere, Jewish people wept, cried out, and prayed. Mordecai cried loudly and bitterly. But Esther, in the palace, knew none of this. Mordecai sent a message, asking her to convince the king to change the decree.

Esther was filled with fear for her people, but she was also afraid for herself. She sent a message back to Mordecai.

Esther: "All the royal servants know that any person who goes to the king without being summoned will be killed unless the king extends his golden scepter. I myself have not been summoned to the king for thirty days. I cannot speak to him."

Narrator: Mordecai knew that only Esther could save them now, so he sent another message. It said, "Perhaps it was for a time like this that you became queen!"

Refrain: Esther, Esther, you must save your people!

Narrator: Esther listened to Mordecai's message, her heart heavy, for she knew Mordecai was right. She told the messenger:

Esther: "Instruct Mordecai to ask all the Jewish people to fast for three days and nights on my behalf. I will, too, and then I will go to the king, despite the law. If I die, I die."

Narrator: Mordecai and all the Jewish people fasted. They cried out with all their strength, for death was staring them in the face. Esther, too, fasted. She took off her queenly clothing, dressing instead in mourning clothes. She smeared ashes on her face, and her lovely hair became wild. She prayed constantly. On the third day, Esther washed and dressed in her most enchanting clothes. Feeling small with fear, she walked into the king's court.

The king looked up, his face full of majestic anger. Who dared to come in here? Queen Esther staggered, her lovely face drained of its color. She fell forward and God changed King Ahasureus's anger to gentleness.

Refrain: Esther, Esther, you must save your people!

Narrator: Anxiously, the king sprang from his throne, taking Esther into his arms. "What is it, Esther? Take courage! You can trust me!" He touched Esther with his scepter, and went on, "Speak to me! Whatever you want, even if it is half my kingdom, it will be granted you!"

Esther (wearily): "If you please, your majesty, come today with Haman to a banquet I have prepared. There I will tell you what I request."

Narrator: The king gladly agreed. That night, he and Haman enjoyed the feast. Again the king turned to Esther, asking her what she requested.

Esther: "If it pleases your majesty, I ask that my life be spared, and I beg that you spare the lives of my people. For my people and I are to be delivered to slaughter and extinction."

Narrator: The king was astonished. "Who and where is the man who has dared to declare this?" he asked.

Esther: "It is this wicked man, Haman."

Narrator: Deeply angered, the king left the room to walk in the palace gardens. Fearing his wrath, Haman stayed with Esther, begging for his life. Desperate, he threw himself at her. The king came back in, and he thought Haman was trying to hurt the queen. Immediately, Haman was arrested, to die as he had wanted Mordecai to die.

King Ahasureus then decreed that the Jewish people would be safe, and Mordecai would have the job Haman held. Together, Mordecai and Esther worked for the welfare of their people.

Refrain: Esther, Esther, we remember how you saved your people!

The Story of Tobias

(based on the book of Tobit)

Introduction

Like the story of Esther, the Book of Tobit is considered a historical story written in literary form. Some of the early Greek Bibles include both of these stories in wisdom writings.

Tobit and his son Tobias are models of wise people. Themes abound, including the importance of observing the laws, doing good works and almsgiving, remaining patient in adversity, respect for parents, and trust in God.

The story is offered here as a play, with a narrator telling the bulk of the tale, and parts for Tobias, Raphael, Tobit, Anna, Raguel, Edna, Sarah, and a demon. Simple costumes could be fashioned from towels, bathrobes, and too-big tee shirts. Props suggested are: a large cardboard fish, bags or backpacks, small plates and cups, a bridal veil or lace curtain, and a low, small table.

The Story Begins

(A low, small table stands on one side of the stage. On it lie a few dishes. A backpack or bag, containing more small dishes sits on it or near it. The bridal veil should be nearby but not visible. The fish can lie on the floor, a distance from the table.)

Narrator (comes out onto the stage alone): Long ago, a young man named Tobias lived with his parents, Tobit and Anna. This is the story of a journey Tobias took for his parents, a journey that proved to be mysterious and wonderful.

(Enter Tobias, Tobit, and Anna. Tobit sits down near the table.)

Narrator: Tobit had become blind and this left him in great despair. Praying that he would die soon, he called Tobias to him.

(Tobias comes to Tobit and kneels before him.)

Narrator: He instructed the young man,

Tobit: "My son, honor your mother. Pray regularly. All your days, keep the Lord's laws. Give to the poor. And, marry a Jewish woman. I must tell you that long ago, I deposited a large sum of money with a relative in the town of Media.

I want you to go there now to get it back. Find a trustworthy man to travel with you and we will pay him well."

(Tobias stands and bids his parents good-bye, then picks up his bag. Anna weeps and waves as Tobias picks up a backpack and walks to the side of the stage. Anna and Tobit walk off stage at the opposite side. Raphael, carrying a bag, enters near Tobias.)

Narrator: Tobias soon met a friendly stranger named Raphael. He was a distant relative, he said, and he knew the way to Media. They journeyed together.

(Tobias and Raphael begin walking together across the stage. They stop near the fish prop.)

Narrator: As night came on, the travelers stopped to camp by the Tigris River. Tobias went down to the water and waded in to soothe his tired feet. Suddenly, he shouted, for a large fish leapt out of the water and attacked him.

(Tobias leans over as if to touch the water, then he picks up the fish prop as if it jumps, and begins to struggle with it. He gives a cry of alarm.)

Raphael: "Do not let it get away! Take hold of it!"

Narrator: Despite his fright, Tobias managed to do what Raphael directed, and brought the fish to him. When Tobias knelt down to clean the fish, Raphael said,

Raphael: "Set aside the gall and liver for medicines. The rest will make us a fine meal."

(Raphael gets out plates from the bags as Tobias prepares the fish. They eat, then lie down to sleep. Raphael gets up first.)

Narrator: After a restful sleep, Tobias awoke to find Raphael preparing for the day.

(Raphael sets the dishes out for breakfast. They begin to eat.)

Narrator: As they ate, Tobias asked Raphael about the medicines that could be prepared with the fish. He was surprised by the answer.

Raphael: "If you burn the liver, the smoke will drive away demons. The gall can be rubbed on eyes that have cataracts, and the sight will be restored. Tonight we will reach Media, and will spend the night with Raguel, who is a relative."

(Tobias nods.)

Raphael: "Raguel has a daughter, Sarah, his only child. Your father instructed you to marry a Jewish woman. You should marry her."

Tobias: "I have heard of Sarah. She has tried to marry seven times, but all of her husbands drop dead right after the wedding! There must be a demon who kills them!"

Raphael (shrugs nonchalantly and says): "That is what the fish liver is for.

Marry Sarah, and place the fish liver on the fire. The smoke will scare off the demon."

Narrator: Tobias was not easily convinced, not wanting to become the eighth victim. But Raphael persisted.

Raphael: "Sarah is sensible. She is courageous, and beautiful, too. Don't be afraid. She was set apart for you before the world existed."

Tobias (smiling): "Yes, I will marry Sarah. Let's begin the rest of our journey."

(They pack up, and leave the stage. Raguel, Edna, and Sarah enter from the other side, sitting down near the table. Tobias and Raphael enter, as if approaching the house. They knock, and the family welcomes them with embraces. They all sit together and eat.)

Narrator: Raguel and his family were delighted to meet Tobias and Raphael. They spoke of Tobit's blindness with sadness. But soon they feasted. Raphael asked Raguel's permission for Tobias to marry Sarah. Raguel and Edna warned of the demon, but like Raphael, they seemed convinced that God would bless this marriage and keep Tobias safe. Raphael retrieved the money they came for and the wedding was held soon.

(Edna places the veil on Sarah's head. Sarah and Tobias go to the side of the stage. A demon enters and stands near them.)

Narrator: That night, Tobias built a small fire and placed the fish liver on it. He and Sarah prayed.

(Tobias bends over as if to start a fire, then he and Sarah pray. The demon jumps up in fright, runs across the stage, exiting the other side.)

The demon left quickly, escaping to Upper Egypt.

Now it was time for the newlyweds to travel to Tobias' home. Sarah's parents gave them blessings and gifts, and said farewell.

(Raguel, Edna, Sarah, and Tobias embrace. Sarah is still wearing the veil.)

Edna: "Tobias, before the Lord, I entrust my daughter to your care. Remember, you are now Sarah's love, and she is your beloved. Go in peace."

(Tobias, Sarah, and Raphael journey across stage. Raguel and Edna wave, then exit.)

Raphael: "You still have the fish gall. When you see your father, Tobias, rub it onto his eyes, and he will see again."

(Enter Tobit and Anna.)

Narrator: When they reached Tobias' home. Raphael and Sarah remained outside, while Tobias went in to greet his parents. Tobit and Anna were overjoyed to have him home again.

(They embrace.)

Tobias: "I am home with the money, but I have much more than that. First, Father, have courage and let me put medicine on your eyes."

(Tobias pats Tobit's closed eyes. Anna watches.)

Tobit: "I can see! Blessed is God and all God's angels! I can see my son!"

Tobias: "Then come see your new daughter-in-law!"

(Tobit and Anna are excited as Tobias leads his parents outside. Tobit and Anna embrace Sarah. Raphael stands back, watching and smiling.)

Tobit: "Welcome, my daughter! Blessed are you and blessed is my son! Blessed be God's name for all these miracles today!"

Anna: "Welcome to your new home. Come, let's celebrate!"

(Anna takes Sarah's arm and they walk back into the house. Tobit and Tobias go to center stage. Raphael remains in the background.)

Tobit: "We'll give Raphael half of the money you brought back."

(Tobias nods and gestures for Raphael to join them. When he does, Tobias holds out his bag to Raphael. Raphael puts up his hands to refuse, and shakes his head.)

Raphael: "No, thank you. Do not pay me. Instead, thank God for all that has been done for you. Never stop praising God. Do good, give alms. Prayer and fasting are good, but giving to others and right behavior are even better. "

(Tobit and Tobias look at one another, puzzled.)

Raphael: "When you saw me eat and drink, you saw a vision. When you prayed to die, Tobit, I was sent to you. For I am Raphael, one of the seven angels who serve the Lord."

(Tobit and Tobias grab each other's arms and back away.)

Raphael (gently): "Do not be afraid. It was God's will that I came to you, so thank God each day. Praise God each day. And now, I must ascend to God."

(Raphael raises his arms and slowly walks off stage. Tobit and Tobias watch him go, then go to Anna and Sarah. They all kneel and pray. Then, they sit, as if to eat.)

Narrator: So, Tobit, who wanted to die, lived happily many more years. As the angel instructed, he sang God's praises, and gave money to the poor. He and Anna were blessed with seeing seven sons born to Sarah and Tobias. They never saw Raphael again, but perhaps one journey with an angel is enough for a lifetime.

The Story of Daniel

(based on Daniel 5, 6)

Introduction

King Nebuchadnezzar of Babylon had ravaged Jerusalem, then he had ordered the best of the Hebrew youth to be brought to him. Already educated and trained in trades or proven in leadership, they were further educated in the Chaldean language, math, and combat. Daniel was one of these young men. Interested in astrology and astronomy, Daniel interpreted dreams for the king, and he quickly rose to a position of honor. Serving under the next three kings, Daniel remained faithful to his God despite his exile.

The book of Daniel takes place during the Babylonian exile, 590 B.C., but was written between 167 and 164 B.C., when the Jewish people were being persecuted again by Antiochus Epiphanes IV. The purpose of the story was to show Daniel's courage and triumph so that others would maintain faith and hope during their trials.

This story can be read by a narrator with everyone present reciting the "chorus." Explain to listeners before reading it that from this story comes a famous expression: "seeing the handwriting on the wall." Ask them to listen for this expression, and to tell you, after the story, what they think it means.

The Story Begins

King Darius paced up and down. His bed lay empty, for there would be no sleep for Darius tonight. How could he have let this happen? Because he, Darius, had been tricked, Daniel might be dead now. How could he have made such a mistake? The only hope was that this God of Daniel's would save him. Daniel, the intelligent, wise man who had counseled him these years, must not die! And yet, how could he not? Darius himself had had him thrown into a pit of hungry lions.

Chorus: Oh Daniel, your God, whom you have served so faithfully, will have to save you.

Daniel was a Jew who had been forced to leave his home in Jerusalem to live in

Babylon and serve the king years before, during Nebuchadnezzar's reign. Daniel had interpreted that king's dreams. When King Belshazzar, the next king, held a great banquet, Daniel's powers were once again made known. During the feasting and singing, a hush suddenly fell over the crowd. For on the wall, just behind the lamp stand, a human hand appeared and began writing on the wall! It wrote words that no one could read.

King Belshazzar turned pale and trembled. He promised great rewards to anyone who could tell him what it meant. The queen remembered Daniel's powers, and so he was brought in.

Chorus: Oh Daniel, your God, whom you have served so faithfully, will have to save you.

Daniel stood quietly and looked at the handwriting on the wall. "Mene, Mene, Tekel, and Parsin. All three words represent weights," Daniel read. "Oh great king, it means this: 'mene' means God has numbered the days of your kingdom and brought it to an end; 'tekel' means you have been weighed on the scales and found wanting; 'parsin' means your kingdom will be divided and given to two other kingdoms."

And Daniel had been right. King Darius began pacing quicker, remembering that King Belshazzar had been killed that very night of the handwriting, and now he, King Darius, was here because the kingdom had been divided.

Daniel had been so skilled, so intelligent, that Darius, after becoming king, had given him much power. Daniel did well in his role, but others, Darius saw now, were jealous. Leaders called governors, who also had power but not as much as Daniel, tried to dishonor Daniel, but they had not found a way. Until now.

Chorus: Oh Daniel, your God, whom you have served so faithfully, will have to save you.

They had come to Darius and said, "Oh King Darius, live forever! We governors have agreed that the king should establish a law, that whoever prays to anyone for thirty days, except to you, oh King, shall be thrown into a den of lions. Now, oh king, sign the document so that it cannot be changed."

The idea pleased the king, and he had signed it. Darius groaned now at the memory. He should have guessed that Daniel was a prayerful man!

Daniel had continued to pray, for as much as Daniel honored the king, he honored God more. Daniel knew of the law, but his love for God was so great, he risked punishment and prayed as usual. And of course, the governors had been watching.

They had come triumphantly to the king and told him of Daniel's prayers. Oh, the anguish Darius had felt! He couldn't let Daniel die! All day, until sunset, Darius had thought and plotted, trying to find a way to save Daniel. But once a law was put into effect, not even the king could undo it. Daniel was thrown into the pit of hungry lions.

Darius's parting words to Daniel were:

Chorus: Oh Daniel, your God, whom you have served so faithfully, will have to save you.

The king had gone back to the palace, where he vowed he would not eat, but fast until dawn. Sleep would not come. He paced instead.

Finally, the first faint streaks of light touched the eastern sky. Darius was down the steps and out of the palace in minutes. He hastened to the lion's pit. He would call to Daniel. Oh, please, Daniel's God, let there be an answer!

Yet, how could there be?

The king shouted, anguish straining his voice. "Daniel! Servant of the living God! Has your God been able to save you?"

From the depths of the pit came Daniel's voice, "O king, live for ever! My God sent his angel who sealed the lions' jaws! I am unhurt, for I am blameless in God's sight, and I have never done you any wrong either, oh king."

Darius was overjoyed and had Daniel released.

Soon after, the king sent out a decree to all his people that said, "May peace be with you! Let all my empire know Daniel's God, for this God saves, sets free, and works signs and wonder in the heavens and on earth. This God has saved Daniel from the power of the lions."

And the faithful Daniel flourished during the reign of King Darius, and on into the reign of the next king.

Chorus: Oh Daniel, your God, whom you have served so faithfully, has saved you.

The Story of Elizabeth and Zechariah

(based on Luke 1:5–14)

Introduction

All of the previous stories introduce people who came before Jesus, telling of God's saving work in the history of Israel. However, it is John the Baptist who is specifically referred to as the one who went before Jesus, making the way for his public life. But he is not Jesus' ancestor and did not precede him by years. John was Jesus' cousin, born within months of Jesus. When the angel Gabriel told John's father, Zechariah, of John's eventual birth, Gabriel compared John to the prophet Elijah: even before birth, John was filled with the Holy Spirit (it is here that the Holy Spirit is first mentioned). And in true prophetic spirit, the unborn John leapt within Elizabeth's womb when Mary, carrying the unborn Jesus, approached them.

Like many before them, Elizabeth and Zechariah waited for many years to be blessed with a child. They may even have given up hope. When the news came that they were to have a son, it was so surprising, it rendered Zechariah speechless.

John the Baptist plays an important role in the New Testament. After this story, ask listeners who this baby will be. If possible, show them a picture from a children's Bible of John the Baptist. Tell them of John's role of preparing the way for Christ, of his baptizing his cousin Jesus.

The Story Begins

Elizabeth looked up, startled at Zechariah's noisy entrance. He was usually a calm, orderly man. But there he stood, hair disheveled, hands trembling. His eyes had an almost glazed look. "What is it? What happened?" she asked, hurrying to his side.

Zechariah shook his head. He opened his mouth and then closed it again. Holding his hands out in an open gesture, he looked up as if in prayer. He seemed both frustrated and excited.

"What is it? Zechariah, don't keep me in suspense!" Elizabeth pleaded. She took hold of both of his hands and gazed steadily into his eyes. She had never seen her husband so agitated and she and Zechariah had been together for a long time. "What is it, dear?" she asked again, trying to keep her voice level. "Has something happened at the temple?"

He nodded.

"Can you tell me?"

He shook his head, pointing to his throat and shaking his head again.

"Does your throat hurt? Did you eat something that has harmed you—oh, has someone tried to hurt you?"

This time he shook his head vigorously. Then, calmer, he put both of his weathered hands on her cheeks. She could only look at him quizzically. He smiled upon her with love, stroked her cheek, and pointed to her abdomen. She backed away and looked down at her body, then back at Zechariah.

"I don't understand. Why don't you speak? You have never been at a loss for words!"

Zechariah gave a noiseless laugh.

This alarmed Elizabeth greatly. "What is wrong with your voice?" she demanded. He was frustrated now and looked around. Frowning, he turned and reached for the writing tablet.

"You really cannot talk," Elizabeth breathed, bringing her clasped hands to her mouth.

Zechariah sat down and began to draw. Elizabeth stood at his shoulder. As she watched, her eyes widened and she trembled. On the tablet he had drawn an angel.

"You saw an angel, Zechariah?" Her voice was a whisper.

He nodded quickly.

"Were you alone?"

Another nod. He made a simple drawing of a temple and an incense burner.

"You were alone in the sanctuary. It was your time to burn incense?"

Another nod. Then he drew a baby, and pointed to her.

Elizabeth frowned. "How I wish I could read!" she lamented.

Zechariah tapped the drawing of the angel, then the baby, and then tapped Elizabeth's abdomen.

"Oh, I want to understand!" Elizabeth wailed.

Zechariah repeated his tapping.

"Angel…baby…me," Elizabeth said.

Then she gasped.

"Baby…me? An angel told you I will have a baby?" She spoke as if the words were fragile.

Zechariah leaped up, nodding, and threw his arms around her. They twirled together, two people too old to have a baby.

When they stopped, Elizabeth gasped a bit and exclaimed, "A baby! We've waited so long. We've prayed so hard. The humiliation we have suffered! But a baby, me, Zechariah?"

He laughed his soundless laugh and pointed to himself.

"Oh yes, you and I, Zechariah, at our age, at long last, a baby!" She clasped her hands and fell silent, in a prayer of gratitude. Zechariah stood with her. Then she turned to him. "Did the angel say if the baby is a boy or a girl?"

Zechariah nodded.

"Boy?" Another nod. "A boy," she said, savoring the sound. "A child, oh Zechariah, we are truly blessed! He must be a very special child, that an angel of God came to tell you about him!"

Zechariah nodded vigorously.

"We must name him Zechariah." He shook his head. "Why not? Do you want to use your father's name?"

His answer was a strong shaking of his head, and he pointed to the angel on the tablet. For a moment, Elizabeth puzzled. Then slowly she said, "The angel gave you a name too?" A smile and a nod. "What is it?"

Zechariah looked anguished. He could not tell her and Elizabeth could not read. "You know, but you have no way of telling me?"

He smiled sadly. She sighed. Then she looked up at him. "And why can't you talk?" He shrugged, and tapped the angel drawing.

"Something with the angel," she mused. Then alarm rose in her voice. "Zechariah, will you always be speechless? Will our child have a silent father?"

He smiled and shook his head. She smiled back, relieved.

"Well, this certainly is the most astounding day. A baby! A son! And you've been visited by an angel! And you, silent for a time! Why you are, I don't know," she pondered. "Oh, Zechariah, the Lord has looked upon us this day! Imagine, me, an old woman to carry life!"

He looked at her, his eyes full of love. Then they laughed, and he threw his arms around her. They laughed and cried and laughed again.

The Story of Mary

(based on Luke 1:26–38)

Introduction

Christ's closest ancestor was his mother. A very young woman when she began this extraordinary life, she has become one of our greatest models of accepting God's plan for our lives. Much has been written about Mary through legend and traditions, as well as in Scripture. This story looks at the moment when she states her commitment to God's will, when she says yes to being the mother of the child Jesus.

This story can be read by a narrator straight through or by a narrator and five readers. If using readers, practice beforehand. After the reading, explain that the Hail Mary summarizes the angel's greeting to Mary. Then pray it together.

The Story Begins

Narrator: Mary crouched down to the supply of corn, scooped some out, and scattered it on the millstone. She began grinding, her hands quick and skilled. She would make some lentils, too, for her meal with her parents. Mary did much of the food preparations now that she was thirteen, for soon she would be making meals in her own house, the home Joseph was preparing for her.

Reader One: Mary thought of Joseph, that good man her parents had so carefully chosen to marry her. Joseph was a carpenter, a woodcarver. Mary had seen his work, and knew he would make beautiful things for their home. They would not be wealthy, but Joseph made an honest living.

More importantly, she knew he was a kind and gentle man. And he was very prayerful. Together they would lead a life of God's calling.

Reader Two: The light from the open doorway was suddenly blocked. Mary looked up, expecting to see her mother entering. Instead, there stood an angel.

In a rich, full voice, the angel, who was Gabriel, greeted her. "Rejoice, so highly favored one! The Lord is with you!"

Mary stood up, her legs shaking. She could feel her heart pounding. What did this greeting mean? The angel Gabriel went on, "Mary, do not be afraid."

This angel knows my name, Mary thought. And I'm not sure if I can stop being fearful!

Reader Three: "You have won God's favor," Gabriel said. "Listen! You are to conceive and have a son, and you must name him Jesus, for it means 'God saves.' He will be great and will be called Son of the Most High. The Lord God will give him the throne of his ancestor David. He will rule over the House of Jacob forever and his reign will have no end."

Reader Four: Mary was stunned. It was too much to understand all at once! She must ask a question, if she could find her voice.

"How?" she ventured. "How can this all come about? I am not married yet."

"The Holy Spirit will come to you," the angel explained. "So this child will be holy. He will be called the Son of God."

Mary leaned against the table, trying to take it all in.

Reader Five: Gabriel added, "Your cousin Elizabeth has, in her old age, also conceived a son, for nothing is impossible with God."

Mary looked at the angel, and the angel looked at Mary.

"I am the servant of the Lord," Mary accepted. "Let all you say happen." With that, Gabriel disappeared.

Narrator: The house seemed very empty without the presence of the angel. Mary pondered what she had just heard.

A baby? A son, who was to be great. He would reign forever? She didn't understand, yet. What would Joseph say? Would he understand? Would he raise this child with her?

What would the next months bring? What would the next years be like? She didn't know, but she had said yes to it. She had said yes to God.

And what was this about Elizabeth? She, too, was to have a baby? At her age! She and Zechariah must be thrilled. That child to come must be holy too, for the angel had spoken of him. She thought of the angel's words, all of them. Her heart pounded again.

"I will go see Elizabeth," Mary decided. "Elizabeth will understand."

The Story of Joseph

(based on Matthew 1:18–25)

Introduction

Joseph, the husband of Mary, was the protector, guide, and nurturer of the child Jesus, along with Mary. In Scripture, he appears only in Jesus' early life, leading biblical scholars to believe he died before Jesus began his public life. His presence in Jesus' early life was very significant, however. So important was Joseph that he was guided by an angel when critical decisions about the child were to be made. This story tells of his first angelic encounter.

Most of this story takes place within Joseph's thoughts. To emphasize the importance of the angel's words, choose another person to stand and read the angel's lines. Both the main reader and the angel's part should be read over in advance. Don't forget to read with all the emotion Joseph must have been feeling!

The Story Begins

In the flat-roofed, mud and straw house belonging to the woodcarver Joseph, the sound of sawing and hammering could be heard. Outside, children played and called, mothers cooked, other tradespeople in nearby houses were busy at work.

Under Joseph's work-roughened but gentle hands, a table was taking shape. The small room smelled of wood shavings. Joseph's saw, adz, and drill lay nearby.

Joseph put down his saw, and rubbed the back of his neck. It was much too early to quit working, he had other projects to finish. But Joseph had no heart for his work today. Everything that had made sense a few days ago had all changed, and he had a difficult decision to make. Besides, what was the point of finishing the table? It was supposed to be for Mary.

Joseph had agreed, less than a year ago, to marry a young woman. Mary's parents had made the betrothal with him. It was made public, everyone knew that a wedding would take place a year after the agreement. It had been a good time for Joseph as he prepared a home for Mary. She was young, but she was intelligent, gentle, and prayerful. Joseph knew they would build a life together based on God's love.

He ached as he thought of her now.

Mary was with child. And the child was not his. How could this be? Mary would not have betrayed him and gone to another man. And yet, the fact remained, she carried a child now. Hurt as he was, Joseph would not publicly embarrass her. Of course he could not marry her, but he could break his ties with her quietly.

What else could he do? He would go tomorrow to their home and end the commitment. With a sigh, Joseph went back to work, choosing a different project. Perhaps if he worked hard, he would be able to sleep tonight. He did fall asleep after a light supper. He turned over once, twice. And he began to dream. There, in his dream, stood a magnificent angel. The angel spoke.

Angel: "Joseph, son of David!"

The sleeping Joseph sat up in his dream. He did not want to meet an angel lying down.

Angel: "Do not be afraid to take Mary home as your wife. The child within her has been conceived by the Holy Spirit."

Joseph stared at the angel. First an angel, and now this news!

Angel: "She will give birth to a son and you must name him Jesus, because he is the one who is to save his people from their sins. He will also be called Emmanuel, which means 'God-With-Us.'"

Then the angel was gone, and Joseph woke up. He sat up and looked around, bewildered. The dream came back to him slowly. "Do not be afraid to take Mary home." Relief spread through Joseph like a healing spring over dry stones. He wanted to shout, to dance, to go to Mary right now!

"The child within her has been conceived by the Holy Spirit." Those words came back to him. The relief he felt changed to awe and then to fear. An angel had come to him! What kind of holy woman was Mary for this to happen? What kind of life would they lead? What kind of child would this be, with such beginnings? The angel had said, "He is the one who is to save his people from their sins." Who was this child, with such a calling ahead of him?

Joseph lay back down, exhausted. Of course he would marry Mary, of course he would care for the child. He would provide for them, protect them. The angel said the baby would be a boy. He would teach him his woodworking trade. And together, he and Mary would love this special child.

Joseph lay very still, listening to the night sounds for a long time.

The Story of Jesus

(Based on Luke 2:1–20)

Introduction

All the thousands of years of waiting for the Messiah had come to an end. Abraham and Sarah's faithfulness, Rachel and Leah's sacrifices, Joseph's dreams, David's reign, Isaiah's prophecies, Jonah's trials, Esther's courage, all led to the moment in Bethlehem when the Christ Child would be born. And for the readers of these stories, all of Advent, the time of waiting, has passed. It is now the miraculous night when the darkness is over, for "a child is born for us, a son given us."

This story will be familiar to listeners. If you own a crèche set, the statues could be given to listeners, and when each character is introduced (including the sheep and other animals), the listener holding the statue could place the statue in or near the stable. If statues aren't available (or are breakable), simple crowns depicting the characters could be made to substitute.

The Story Begins

"Is it true, Joseph?" Mary asked, the jug of water still sloshing. She had just come in from drawing water at the well. Joseph was drilling a piece of wood. "Must we travel to Bethlehem?"

Joseph put his tool down and looked sadly at Mary. "Yes, I'm afraid so. I just heard too. Every fourteen years the emperor wants a census taken so no one person can go untaxed. As we are of the family of David, we must go to Bethlehem to be registered."

Mary sighed and sat down. Her young body was heavy with the child to come.

"I'm sorry, Mary, with the baby due so soon, it will be very hard for you. He will probably be born there. I'll do the best I can to make you comfortable," the gentle Joseph promised. "But I am very sorry it happened like this."

"Well, maybe this is part of God's plan, too," she answered, and started preparing their meal.

They began their journey early the next morning. Mary packed food and cloths to wrap the baby in. Joseph readied the donkey with other supplies. When she had what they needed, Mary went to the door and turned to look at the home she and Joseph had made together. When they returned, she would have a son to bring into the house. She closed the door and joined Joseph.

The donkey was a good, dependable little animal but just getting up onto him was difficult for Mary. Joseph helped settle his wife, then squeezed her hand and smiled at her. Despite her discomfort, she had to smile back.

For three days they traveled. Mary rode the donkey while Joseph walked, leading it. They crossed the boggy Plain of Esdraelon and the Judaean plateau. All around them were other travelers, and they joined together, talking. Often they laughed, often they complained. Everyone's life had been disrupted for the census that would only bring them taxes. Mary knew Joseph was glad for the company, for traveling could be dangerous. Thieves roamed the hills, as did dangerous animals. Jackals and hyenas were not uncommon.

Mary appreciated the sympathetic looks and smiles from the other women who saw that her baby would come soon. They understood her difficulties, knew she wished that she was home. Still, she would be glad when they got to Bethlehem, where she and Joseph could find a room and be alone.

Bethlehem was on a hill, and the little donkey struggled up it heroically. Mary felt each step, for she now had begun her labor. She knew this was just the beginning, but within hours, she would need to be lying down.

The town was crowded, much more crowded than the roads they had taken this far. Travelers from all over, as well as cattle, camels, mules, and donkeys, filled the streets. The noise was deafening. Mary rubbed her abdomen and closed her eyes for a moment. She did not see the worried look on Joseph's face.

She remained on the donkey as Joseph made his way through the crowd to the door of the inn. He knocked, spoke briefly to the innkeeper, then returned to Mary.

"They have no more room. They are completely full. The innkeeper said they are bedding down people in the courtyard—" Joseph began explaining.

A labor pain overcame her like a wave and Mary gasped, closing her eyes.

Alarmed, Joseph, said, "It is closer than I thought!"

"This is the first pain like this," she said.

"I must think," Joseph said anxiously. "Don't fall off the donkey! I will be right back!"

He hurried into the crowd, again speaking to the innkeeper. Mary saw the man point to the back of the inn, and Joseph thanked him.

"I've got a place. It's with animals, but there are no people. It will be private," Joseph said when he returned. He began leading the donkey as swiftly as he could through the crowds.

Another pain overcame Mary and she did not answer.

This place was just a simple stable in which a patient ox chewed hay, but both Mary and Joseph were glad to see it. Quickly Joseph scooped up clean hay, and spread their blanket upon this. Then he helped Mary down from the donkey and to the bed he had prepared. He led the tired donkey to the corner, and hurried back to Mary.

"Oh, Joseph," Mary said, the difficulties of the past three days welling up in her.

He stroked her cheek. "We're alone now. It's the best we can do. I'm here for you."

Another pain came.

Hours passed this way. Joseph was encouraging, calm, strong. Mary accepted pain after pain. And then, when the time was right, the baby was born. The miracle happened: God became human.

"He is breathing, Mary, he looks healthy—it is a boy," Joseph said, adding, "Of course."

He held the baby close to Mary so she could see him in the darkness.

"He's beautiful!" she said, reaching for him. "Little Jesus, just as the angel promised. Oh, Joseph, he's beautiful!"

In the darkness, Mary could feel Joseph's smile.

They washed the baby, and Mary wrapped him in the cloths she had brought. Then the baby closed his eyes.

"We'd better sleep, too," Joseph said.

"I'm afraid one of the animals might step on him," Mary said. "Let's put him in the manger while we sleep."

A few hours later, Joseph awoke to the sight of a torch coming up the hill toward them. Mary sat up too. It seemed to be a group of shepherds.

"Hello?" one of them called softly. "We don't mean to disturb you, but is there a baby here?"

Joseph stood up, asking, "Is there something you want?"

Another shepherd explained, shyly, "We were tending our sheep when…

when…well, we had a vision. An angel came and told us that a baby had been born here tonight, a child who would save us!"

"The angel said the baby would be lying in a manger, so we thought here might be…" he trailed off, embarrassed.

"Many more angels came then too, singing God's praises," the first shepherd said. "It was so glorious, we thought…"

Mary said, "Come in! Here is the child, and he is in the manger."

The men, humble, rough shepherds, crowded in. They seemed filled with the awe of the angels, which both Mary and Joseph understood. When the shepherds saw the sleeping Jesus, they were silent and prayerful. Then, each one began praising and glorifying God. As they went back down the hill, Joseph stood in the doorway, watching them go and wondering what would happen next.

Mary picked up the now waking baby. She held him close and stroked his small back. So there had been more angels—angels that came to strangers and announced her baby would save them! What did this mean? She treasured all these things and pondered them in her heart.

Suggested Readings

Anderson, Raymond and Georgene. *The Jesse Tree, The Heritage of Jesus in Stories and Symbols of Advent for the Family* (Philadelphia: Fortress Press, 1966).

Bach, Alice, and J. Cheryl Exum, illustrations by Leo and Diane Dillon. *Miriam's Well, Stories About Women in the Bible* (New York: Delecorte Press, 1991).

Bach, Alice, and J. Cheryl Exum, illustrations by Leo and Diane Dillon. *Moses' Ark, Stories from the Bible* (New York: Delecorte Press, 1989).

Catholic Biblical Association of America. *The New American Bible, Translated from the Original Languages with Critical Use of All the Ancient Sources* (Washington D.C.: Catholic Educational Guild, 1970).

Chaikin, Miriam, illustrations by Yvonne Gilbert. *Children's Bible Stories from Genesis to Daniel* (New York: Dial, 1993).

Costello, Gwen. *Classroom Prayer Services for the Days of Advent and Lent* (Mystic, CT: Twenty-Third Publications, 1997).

dePaola, Tomie. *Mary, the Mother of Jesus* (New York: Holiday House, 1995).

Farb, Peter, illustrations by Harry McNaught. *The Land, Wildlife, and Peoples of the Bible* (New York: Harper and Row, 1967).

Fuchshuber, Annegert, illustrator, condensed by Rolf E. Aaseng. *Augsburg Story Bible* (Minneapolis: Augsburg, 1992).

Horn, Geoffrey, and Arthur Cavanaugh, illustrated by Arvis Stewart. *Bible Stories for Children* (New York: Macmillan, 1980).

James, Darcy. *Let's Make a Jesse Tree! 26 Full Size Patterns* (Nashville: Abingdon Press, 1987).

Jones, Alexander, ed. *The Jerusalem Bible* (New York: Doubleday and Company, Inc., 1966, 1967, 1968).

Kielly, Shiela and Sheila Geraghty. *Advent and Lent Activities for Children* (Mystic, CT: Twenty-Third Publications, 1996).

National Geographic Society. *Everyday Life in Bible Times* (Washington D.C.: 1967).

Newson, Carol A., and Sharon H. Ringe, eds. *The Women's Bible Commentary* (Louisville: Westminster/John Knox Press, 1992). First published in Great Britain in 1992 by SPCK, Holy Trinity Church, London.

Paterson, Katherine. *The Spying Heart, More Thoughts on Reading and Writing Books for Children* (New York: Dutton, 1989).

Paterson, Jose, illustrated by Claire Bushe. *Angels, Prophets, Rabbis and Kings from the Stories of the Jewish People* (New York: Peter Bedrick Books, 1991).

Spier, Peter. *The Book of Jonah* (New York: Doubleday, 1985).

Wiesel, Elie. *Messengers of God, Biblical Portraits and Legends* (New York: Random House, 1976).

Yolan, Jane. *Touch Magic, Fantasy, Faerie and Folklore in the Literature of Childhood* (New York: Philomel, 1981).

Youngman, Bernard R. *The Lands and People of the Living Bible, a Narrative History of the Old and New Testament.* Edited by Walter Russell Bowie (New York: Hawthorn Books, Inc. 1959).

Of Related Interest...

Advent and Lent Activities for Children
Camels, Carols, Crosses, and Crowns
Shiela Kielly and Sheila Geraghty
This book offers a wealth of information, reflections, activities, and unique ways to share the customs, symbols, and messages of Lent and Advent with children.
ISBN: 0-89622-676-X, 128 pp, $9.95 (order M-51)

On Video...

Angel's Advent Lesson
Gwen Costello
This video captivates children and lets them know that Advent and Christmas are much, much more than just anticipating and enjoying new toys and games. This program educates children, 7 to 12 years old, about the true meaning of Advent and prepares them for a spiritual Christmas. Their companion and guide in discovery is Theo, Danny's guardian angel.
11 minute video, $29.95 (order D–03)

Angel's Lenten Lesson
Gwen Costello
Children learn from one boy's interaction with his guardian angel the meaning of Lent, with many of its symbolic practices. 10-year-old Danny is having trouble with his homework for religion class about lenten practices when, to his surprise, his guardian angel, Theo, appears. She helps Danny remember and appreciate the lenten practices he celebrated the year before, enabling him to finish his homework and come to a greater appreciation of his faith.
14-minute video, $29.95 (order A–58)

The Best Night of the Year
Gwen Costello
This wonderful story for children in grades K through 2 will remind children that the birth of Jesus is what makes Christmas special.
12 minute video, $19.95 (order A-85)

The Gift
Alice Testa
Young children will get a view of the first Christmas from a unique perspective. This is the story of an ordinary little bug who lived in a crack of the Jerusalem wall.
6 minute video, $9.95 (order A-82)

Available at religious bookstores or from:

TWENTY-THIRD PUBLICATIONS
P.O. Box 180 • Mystic, CT 06355

For a complete list of quality books and videos call:
1 - 8 0 0 - 3 2 1 - 0 4 1 1